'So It Was All L...

You were never with ... or any other man, for that matter.' Slowly the words came, and so very quietly.

'Come here, Kim.'

'You—you frighten m-me,' she faltered. 'Please go away and—and leave me alone.'

'I said come here.'

She took another faltering step backwards and it was when her hand touched the door that an incredible transformation took place within her. 'Don't stand there giving me orders! The marriage suited you as much as it suited me, so what's your complaint?'

'My complaint's the deceit—'

ANNE HAMPSON
currently makes her home in Ireland, but this top romance author has travelled and lived all over the world. This variety of experience is reflected in her books, which present the ever-changing face of romance as it is found wherever people fall in love.

Dear Reader:

Silhouette Books is pleased to announce the creation of a new line of contemporary romances—*Silhouette Special Editions*. Each month we'll bring you six new love stories written by the best of today's authors— Janet Dailey, Brooke Hastings, Laura Hardy, Sondra Stanford, Linda Shaw, Patti Beckman, and many others.

Silhouette Special Editions are written with American women in mind; they are for readers who want more: more story, more details and descriptions, more realism, and more *romance*. *Special Editions* are longer than most contemporary romances allowing for a closer look at the relationship between hero and heroine with emphasis on heightened romantic tension and greater sensuous and sensual detail. If you want more from a romance, be sure to look for *Silhouette Special Editions* on sale this February wherever you buy books.

We welcome any suggestions or comments, and I invite you to write us at the address below.

Karen Solem
Editor-in-Chief
Silhouette Books
P.O. Box 769
New York, N. Y. 10019

ANNE HAMPSON
Desire

Silhouette Romance

Published by Silhouette Books New York

America's Publisher of Contemporary Romance

Other Silhouette Romances by Anne Hampson

The Dawn Steals Softly	*Payment in Full*
Enchantment	*Second Tomorrow*
Fascination	*Shadow of Apollo*
Man of the Outback	*Stormy Masquerade*
Man Without a Heart	*Where Eagles Nest*

 SILHOUETTE BOOKS, a Simon & Schuster Division of
GULF & WESTERN CORPORATION
1230 Avenue of the Americas, New York, N.Y. 10020

Copyright © 1981 by Anne Hampson and Silhouette Books,
a Simon & Schuster Division of Gulf & Western Corporation

Distributed by Pocket Books

ISBN: 0-671-57119-2

First Silhouette Books printing December, 1981

10 9 8 7 6 5 4 3 2 1

America's Publisher of Contemporary Romance

Printed in the U.S.A.

Desire

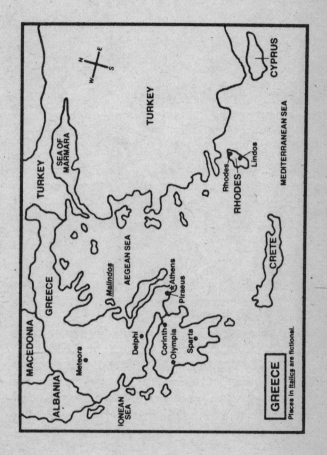

GREECE

Places in italics are fictional.

Chapter One

There was a frown on Kim Rosswell's wide forehead as she put the finishing touches to her pale gold hair, fixing a diamanté stud that was meant to be functional as well as decorative, as it held back an unruly lock which invariably persisted in falling onto her forehead.

Dendras was becoming overinvolved, too emotionally intense. She had considered him a mere boy, not yet of an age to fall in love, but she strongly suspected that tonight he would talk about marriage, and her frown deepened at the idea of hurting him. They had met in the most improbable circumstances when their cars had been locked in a car park belonging to a bank. Kim had to smile at the young man's dismay as he stood staring through the iron railings of the gate, reading the newly erected notice: 'This car park will close at three-thirty.'

Of course, both knew they should not have made use of the park in the first place, and Kim was also aware that the gate was usually locked at half past four each afternoon. Never had she known it to be closed before then, but she surmised at once, as she read the notice, that too many people had been using the park which, quite naturally, was reserved exclusively for the bank's clients.

'What are we going to do?' The young man's brow was puckered and there was a quiver in his accented voice. 'I've been doing some research on this town and there was nowhere else to park my car. I have to be back at the university by half past five.'

'You'll not be able to have your car until after ten o'clock tomorrow morning.' Kim herself was resigned. She lived only a couple of miles from town and could either walk or take a bus. 'You'll have to use a taxi and come back tomorrow.'

He had sighed and moved away. The following morning they met again, each approaching the car park rather furtively in case there was someone waiting to reprimand them for their illegal use of the park. But as luck would have it, they both drove off without incident, only to meet again in a coffee shop an hour later. It was natural that they should nod and smile, and as the cafe was crowded, they found themselves sharing a table.

'It's fate,' declared the young man after spontaneously offering his name. 'How about having lunch with me?'

Kim hesitated, but not for long. She liked the dark eyes, the frank open face of the olive-skinned young man, and as she was on vacation for a week, she had no commitments. Dendras, on the other hand, was supposed to be fully engaged on his research, which was connected with the architecture of the town, but, he said, there was no real pressure. And so they lingered over their coffee, then sauntered around medieval Chester, where Kim was able to point out buildings of particular interest.

'How long have you been at Liverpool?' she asked conversationally, and learned that he was in his final year at the university. 'Why aren't you studying in your own country?' she had enquired.

'I live on an island and we haven't the educational facilities. I could have studied in Athens, but my friends at Liverpool and I wanted to be there, too. It was an idea to which, fortunately, my brother—who is also my guardian—made no objection, so here I am.' He had gazed at her with undisguised admiration later, as they sat opposite one another at the luncheon table, and within the next hour or so she had learned a great deal about Dendras Christou and his elder brother, Vidas. The latter was a stern, unbending man from what Kim could gather, arrogant and rather too aware of his position as owner of a vast citrus- and olive-producing estate and also the Castello Astura, a renovated Venetian castle situated on the breathtakingly beautiful island of Malindos in the Aegean.

'The castle and estate belong entirely to your brother?' Kim looked puzzled as she asked the question. 'You haven't a share in them?'

'Father left them to him because he's the elder. Vidas and I are stepbrothers,' he added inconsequentially.

'And your brother isn't married, you said?'

'He's thirty-five and up till now has shown no interest in marriage.' He stopped rather abruptly, colour mounting into his cheeks. Kim smiled to herself, aware of the reason for his embarrassment. It was a well-known fact that Greek men were the most amorous in the world, so it did not require much imagination to guess that Vidas Christou would not be living the celibate life.

Dendras had asked Kim to go out to dinner with him on the following Saturday and she had agreed; this led to other dates, and now, after almost three months of pleasant friendship, Kim was again meeting him for dinner, her intention being to put an end to the affair before he became even more deeply involved. As it was, his feelings must be hurt, but not overmuch—certainly not as severely as they would be were she to continue seeing him.

She took a last look in the mirror before turning away to pick up her wrap and the evening bag of white satin and sequins, which matched the ankle-length dress she wore. Full-skirted, yet cut on simple lines, it enhanced her slender figure, clinging to her small breasts and waist, then flowing out towards the hem in gentle, exquisitely cut folds. Being white, it lent her delicate features an ethereal quality, which was made even more pronounced by the colour of her hair. In contrast, her eyebrows and lashes were dark, her eyes an unusual colour of smoke blue that seemed at times to change to green. Her full generous mouth was tilted at the corners, her throat white and long above grace-fully sloping shoulders, which at present were bare, the gown being held up by straps no more than a quarter of an inch wide.

She was not surprised by the look of deep admiration that leapt to Dendras's face when they met in the lounge of the Grosvenor Hotel in Chester.

'How beautiful you are!' Dendras's hands were extended to take hers and she coloured despite her composure, for several people were amusedly witnessing the effusive way in which she was being greeted by the dark young man with the foreign voice. 'Kim, I—'

'Shall we order drinks?' she broke in swiftly, leading him gently by the hand towards a low sofa at the far end of the lounge.

'I wanted to call for you.' His voice was petulant as he sat down beside her. 'Why won't you let me come to your home?'

'Because I don't think my parents would approve of my going out with anyone so young.' She had hoped to impart her news in a way that would mitigate the pain as much as possible, but now she doubted her ability to do so.

'I'm almost twenty-one—two years younger than you. It's nothing.'

'It's far too much,' returned Kim gently. 'The man should be older than the woman—in a serious affair, that is.'

He looked at her through bewildered eyes. 'This isn't serious, then?'

'No, Dendras—'

'I was going to ask you to marry me,' he broke in desperately. 'Oh, Kim, you must know that I love you!'

She swallowed the hard little lump that had lodged in her throat, cursing herself for not ending the affair weeks ago.

'It's only calf-love,' she began, still in the same gentle tones, but before she could add anything Dendras was asking, 'What is calf-love? I have never heard the expression.'

She explained, watching him shaking his head.

'I love you properly,' he stated. 'I'm old enough to know my own mind, Kim.'

'Have you ever stopped to consider whether or not your brother would approve of me?'

There was a tense pause before Dendras said, 'I—I've asked him for his consent to—'

'You—!' Kim's eyes widened. 'You've gone as far as to seek his approval of our marriage?' This was much worse than she had suspected, and Kim more than ever blamed herself for allowing the friendship to continue as long as it had.

'Yes, I've been asking him for weeks, phoning almost every day, pleading with him to let me get married but he was adamant—until Thursday, when at last he gave in and said I could marry you.' Dendras swallowed convulsively and Kim suspected it was a nervous gesture even before he turned his head away, hiding his expression from her curious gaze. She stared intently at his profile, her pulses quickening for some reason she failed to understand. Why was he blushing, looking decidedly guilty and avoiding her gaze?

'What made him change his mind?' Kim's tone was unconsciously short.

'I . . . er . . . suppose he realised I was determined.'

'He did?' Kim's eyes still searched his profile. 'Your argument must have carried a great deal more weight on Thursday than at any other time.'

'Of course, or otherwise he'd not have agreed to my marriage.' The air of guilt was still present and it brought the obvious question from his companion.

'What did you say that was so different from what you'd said before?'

Silence, with Dendras shifting about uneasily in his

chair. He looked at her, opened his mouth as if he would blurt something out, then closed it again.

'Aren't you going to answer my question, Dendras?' she prompted him, but he only sighed and shook his head, his whole manner betraying extreme discomfort.

'I didn't say anything different—'

'Dendras,' broke in Kim gently, 'you must have done.'

'I expect he became exasperated and decided to give his consent.' His voice was defiant now, but he again avoided Kim's eyes. 'Vidas hasn't much patience at the best of times and my perseverance must have broken down what little he had.'

Although she was aware that he was lying, Kim could not for the life of her imagine what Dendras could have said to make his brother change his mind. 'You do realise you're being vexingly mysterious,' she just had to say.

'Mysterious?' he asked with well-feigned surprise. 'What makes you say so?' The tone of defiance returned and so did his guilty colour.

'From what little I've gathered about this brother of yours, I'd not have expected him to change his mind once it was made up.' Not unless Dendras had said something which had completely altered the whole aspect of the situation, she mused, a frown creasing her brow.

'I've just said he hasn't much patience.' There was a sulky edge to the tone and a pout on his lips as he added, 'I can't see the reason for your attitude, Kim.'

A deep sigh escaped her and she decided to let the matter drop, and in any case, the waiter was coming to take their order.

As soon as the drinks were brought one of the

restaurant waiters appeared with the menu, and for a few minutes Kim and her companion were silent. But suddenly he lowered the large, leather-enclosed menu and said, with a distinct catch in his voice, 'I was very serious about wanting to marry you, Kim. Please think about it, at least, before you give me a definite refusal.'

She shook her head, biting her lip with vexation at her own stupidity in not making a break long ago, yet admitting that continued self-blame was both futile and unprofitable. 'I'm not in love with you, Dendras, so there's no sense in my even thinking about marriage.'

His face closed; she noticed the throbbing of a nerve in his jaw and wished with all her heart they had never met. Fate, he had called it! Fate could be relentlessly cruel at times.

'I feel utterly lost,' he owned. 'I—I thought you liked m-me.'

'Liking isn't loving,' she pointed out. 'Of course I like you, but there can be nothing serious between us—'

'You're too hasty,' he accused, his dark eyes misted, proving without doubt just how young he was, for it was plain that he was coming dangerously close to tears. 'Don't tell me this is . . . is the end.'

Reluctantly, she nodded her head.

'It is,' she answered, wondering how they would get through the meal. 'Perhaps we should not have dinner after all, but say good-bye now.'

'No! I must see you again—I must!' His mouth twisted and for a space he was unable to speak. 'Have dinner with me,' he begged at last, a plea in his eyes. Kim shook her head; it was a gesture of impatience rather than a denial. But it seemed to bring him to his senses; she saw him straighten up to square his shoulders. He pulled himself together and said, 'I'll not mention it again this evening, Kim, I promise. Let us enjoy our meal as we always have.'

'All right.' She was gratified to note his response to her smile, aware that he was determined to throw off his dejection, and so they were able to chat over the meal in the usual carefree and pleasant way. She had already learned much about his home on the island of Malindos—the lovely renovated castle so tastefully furnished and so magnificently situated on a wooded plateau overlooking the Aegean Sea. She knew it was mellowed with age, its interior boasting all that was luxurious and elegant, suggesting, as it should, an air of gracious living. And now Dendras was telling her about the grounds, his descriptions so vivid that she could almost see the way the morning sunshine on the dew lent a star-spangled effect to the mile-long avenue of plane trees leading up to the imposing front entrance of the castle, their branches closing overhead. She could easily imagine the masses of gaudy, opulent hibiscus bushes, the ancient, massive carob dominating the view from one of the windows of the main dining salon, the crystal spray of the fountains and the marble goddesses standing guard beside them. She learnt that Dendras's mother kept house for her stepson, running it with a sort of rigid efficiency.

'Father stipulated that Mother must remain at the Castello, as its mistress, until Vidas marries,' Dendras said, and there was an undercurrent to his voice that caused Kim to sense that Vidas was not at all happy with the terms of his father's will.

Dendras changed the subject before Kim could ask any questions and she heard about the landscape of the island, which despite its small size was mountainous

and even barren in parts. But it was said to be one of
the most spectacularly beautiful islands of its group,
rivalled only by Rhodes in the variety of colour and
vegetation. Even the barren parts lent beauty, rising as
they did above the valley, their high summits clear-cut
against the sky.

'Have you ever been to Greece?' Dendras's voice
had become more noticeably accented, owing to the
enthusiasm he felt as he described his island home to
the girl whose interest had been well and truly caught.

'No, never,' she replied, wondering if she would ever
have the money for a trip to the country that had
intrigued her ever since, as a small girl at school, she
had pored over colourfully illustrated stories of Jason
and the Golden Fleece, and Odysseus outwitting the
sirens. For her, Greece would always have the same
fascination as it had then; it was a fabled, mystic land of
pagan gods and fearless heroes, of history and culture,
its ancient peoples having brought civilisation to the
Western world. 'One day perhaps I shall visit it,' she
added at length. 'Malindos sounds particularly intrigu-
ing and beautiful.'

'Many Greek islands are just as beautiful, but in a
different way. If you ever come to my island . . .' His
voice trailed off as shadows touched his eyes. But when
presently he spoke again, there was nothing in his voice
to betray his inner feelings. 'You must go to the lovely
bays along the southern coast. They are often deserted
because our island is not geared to tourism like some of
the larger ones.' He described the Halthea Valley,
much of which was owned by his brother, who grew
fruit and olives for export. 'In another, narrower valley
you would see the remains of many Venetian castles
which might one day be restored like ours. At the head

16

of this valley, on the cliff, is another magnificent castle owned by a Greek who married an Irish girl.'

'An Irish girl? She managed to settle, then?'

'She is in love,' returned Dendras simply.

Love . . . An involuntary sigh issued from Kim's lips. Would love ever come to her? She had dreams, like any other girl, but as yet she had never met a man she liked enough to encourage. She often wondered if she was too choosey, because she had had several opportunities for going steady but had turned them all down.

'Is there any kind of industry on the island?' she asked when the silence began to stretch. 'Do they grow anything as a staple?'

'No, not as such. We have a few hotels now springing up, and there are the fruit and the olives.' He paused and then, with a faint, rather faraway smile, said, 'I haven't told you of the strange custom that somehow came into being in my family, have I?'

'No.' Kim looked interested. 'Tell me about it.'

'Well, there is an unwritten law in my family that puts an obligation on male members to see that any girl who becomes pregnant must never be left in the lurch—' He stopped, his young face gaining colour. 'It's a crude way of putting it, isn't it?'

'Using the term "left in the lurch" you mean?' Kim laughed and shook her head. 'I don't think so, Dendras.'

'Well, to continue. If one member of my family should die after getting a girl in the family way it's incumbent on another to marry her, be it a brother or cousin.'

Kim could only stare disbelievingly for a long moment before saying, 'What a fantastic custom! What would happen if there wasn't a male free to marry the girl? I mean, they all might be married.'

'To be honest, I don't think the custom has ever been put into operation—if that's how one would put it.' Dendras laughed. 'All our men must have lived to marry the girls if ever they did get them into that position. . . .' For some reason he allowed his voice to trail off into silence, yet again he deliberately avoided Kim's eyes. She frowned at his strangeness, and felt the hair on her forearms lift as her nerves tensed involuntarily.

'Dendras,' she said, 'I don't understand you at all. Are you serious about this custom you mention?'

'Of course,' he replied indignantly. 'It's the truth. I expect it does sound silly but, after all, it would be just a matter of honour, wouldn't it?'

'So you say; I still don't understand your manner.'

He coloured, but managed to appear cool and controlled. 'Forget it,' he said, taking a crusty roll from the basket. 'Vidas is always saying he'll revoke it, but of course he hasn't bothered because he knows he'll never have to honour it.'

Kim looked at him, her frown deepening. 'Do you mean to say that as things are at present, if you—' She stopped and now it was her turn to colour up.

Toying with the roll on his plate, Dendras said, 'Yes, if I got a girl into the family way and then died, he would have to marry her in order to give the child a name.'

'Well, of all the stupid customs! It's beyond belief!'

'No such thing. The same custom existed in France for a very long period. It might still exist in some families.'

18

Kim merely shrugged and changed the subject, asking Dendras to tell her more about his home, but he talked about his brother instead, saying that he lived for his business and had little time for relaxation.

'He has a study in a quiet part of the house and spends a good deal of his time there. Of course, he has a lady friend now and then—I expect you gathered that from what I said earlier?'

'From the way you acted,' corrected Kim. 'I believe all Greek men have lady friends, whether they are married or not?'

'Their wives often have lovers too,' returned Dendras. 'Morals are not thought much of in Greece.'

'Your brother's fifteen years older than you, I think you said?'

'That's right, and so Father made him my trustee until I'm twenty-one. Vidas has the Castello and the land, but I have a large fortune, and this is being looked after by Vidas. I was only sixteen when Father died.'

'If your brother's as old as that, it's a wonder he isn't married. Surely he wants an heir to all that wealth?'

'He might marry one day. But I suppose he feels sure that I will eventually provide an heir.' He paused in thought. 'If I did have a son, I don't think Vidas would ever get married, because he seems more than satisfied with his bachelor existence.' Dendras looked fixedly at her, stressing the words as a tacit reminder that she was being offered the honour of mothering the heir to the Christou wealth. 'Yes, Vidas would be more than pleased if I were to produce a son.'

Kim said casually, 'Tell me about your mother. I've noticed that you haven't said much about her at all.'

'For a reason.' His foreign voice was almost harsh.

'I'd rather not talk about my mother. She and Vidas are two of a kind—hard and unfeeling, unapproachable.'

'I'm sorry,' she murmured, faintly shocked at the dramatic change in Dendras's manner. 'Forgive me—'

'It's all right. You weren't to know that we don't see eye to eye.'

A thoughtful expression settled on Kim's face as a result of what Dendras had just said. She was thinking of his brother and wondering how he got on with his stepmother, who had the right to remain in his home until he married. Kim had previously sensed that Vidas was not too happy with the arrangement, but she supposed he must get along all right with the woman or he'd have married before now, if only to rid himself of her presence in his home.

But even as she was reaching this conclusion she heard Dendras say, 'Vidas doesn't get on with her either. She can be exceedingly awkward and determined, but he has no alternative than to put up with her.'

'You'd think he would get married, then.'

Dendras only shrugged and the subject was changed. However, Kim could not help dwelling on the matter and feeling puzzled that Vidas didn't decide to marry and free himself of what seemed to be a burden.

Later, when she and Dendras were saying good night by her car, which was parked close to his, she heard his plea and a sigh left her lips.

'I can't let you go like this, Kim—never to see you again. Please say we can meet and have dinner as usual next Saturday?'

She looked at him in the hotel's bright light, knowing what she ought to do and yet acutely conscious of what her soft heart was urging her to do—and the two were vastly different.

'It isn't going to do any good,' she began when, to her consternation, he started to cry. 'All right,' she amended swiftly, 'I'll see you on Saturday.'

'Here, at the Grosvenor, or would you like to go somewhere else for a change?'

'Let's meet at the Adelphi in Liverpool. It's an excellent place to dine.'

'It's such a long way for you to drive,' he protested.

'No such thing—just about an hour even if the traffic's heavy.'

And so it was arranged; they were to meet in the lobby of the Adelphi the following Saturday. This time Kim wore a rather slinky dress of turquoise satin with slits up both sides of the skirt. She had never liked the dress but decided she must get some wear out of it nevertheless. It made her appear older and more worldly, and when she looked at herself in the long mirror as she entered the hotel, she wished fervently she had worn something else.

To her surprise Dendras was not there, but just as she was about to sit down to wait, he appeared. He was not alone.

Walking beside him was a tall dark foreigner, lithe of frame and stern of feature, arrogance and good breeding in every majestic step he took. People turned their heads to follow his progress; he seemed to dominate the entire scene, and Kim, knowing instinctively who he was, likened him to some powerful Greek god, even the great Zeus himself.

'Kim, meet Vidas!' Dendras's words came swiftly; he was shy, unsure of himself in his brother's presence, and Kim could very well understand why. Vidas

21

Christou was the most impressive, and at the same time forbidding, man she had ever set eyes on. Well over six feet in height, he had the gait and form of an athlete in his prime. His dark aquiline features seemed to stamp themselves on her mind even before she had time to examine them. She was fascinated by his eyes; they were almost black and hooded, which gave them a lazy expression, while, conversely, they were piercing and shrewd, eyes that would miss nothing. His skin was clear and brown, tightly stretched above facial hollows so that the high cheekbones were accentuated, as were the rigid jawline and outthrust chin. His mouth was thin and yet sensuous, his nose straight, with fine nostrils that appeared to be flaring as he stared down at Kim, one lean brown hand extended, ready to grip hers. Contempt was spread over his face, and it was plain that he disliked her on sight—just as she disliked him, intensely. He seemed rather older than his thirty-five years, and Kim spitefully put this down to his amorous exploits.

'How do you do?' he said in a deep foreign voice. 'So you have been keeping company with my brother?' The dark eyes slid in almost insolent examination from her face to the low neckline of the dress and down to where one of the slits revealed a shapely leg from the ankle to the thigh. She went hot all over, lowering her eyes against the undisguised scorn in his. But she remained conscious of those dark eyes burning into her bare shoulders, then settling on the seductive valley between her barely covered breasts. Dendras was shifting uncomfortably on his feet, and when at last his voice was heard, it was cracked and urgent.

'Vidas arrived unexpectedly this morning, so I—I

asked him to come along and meet you—' His eyes roamed over her figure, puzzlement and censure in their depths. 'He's dining with us, Kim. I've booked a table for three instead of two.'

'I see.' She was enveloped in guilt without knowing why; all she did know was that never in her life had she felt so small and cheap, so totally lacking in self-assurance. This man, with his air of severe austerity, was deliberately disconcerting her; she was sure of it even before he said, in a voice rather less accented than his brother's, 'I expected to meet someone much younger. Do you mind telling me your age?'

Her eyes glinted, anger surging within her. 'I would rather not,' she answered shortly.

The hooded Greek eyes fixed hers in a narrowed humorless stare. 'I suspect you are at least eight years older than my brother.'

Kim's temper flared. She might look older than her years at this moment, but she was sure she did not appear to be approaching thirty! 'You can suggest what you like,' she seethed, conscious even in her anger of the man's attractions, his noble features, his superlative physique . . . plus a strange magnetism that drew and held her even in the face of her profound dislike of him.

'Vidas didn't mean anything insulting,' Dendras interposed unhappily. 'Shall we have a drink?' Imploring eyes sought those of his brother, who stared at him inscrutably without replying. 'It's not much fun just standing here, is it?'

Vidas nodded, then smiled unexpectedly. 'You're quite right,' he agreed. 'Let us go into the lounge.'

It was inevitable that the meal would be a failure, for

neither Kim nor Dendras was at ease. Vidas spoke a great deal, mainly to ask Kim about herself and her family. She answered, fully aware that he was baiting her, having been given the wrong impression by Dendras. He wanted to know all about her, believing she wanted to marry his brother. And while the kind and obvious course would have been to disillusion him, some imp of mischief, born of her dislike, impelled her to remain silent about her intentions regarding his brother. Let him worry! She hoped he'd lie awake all night!

'Why did he come over?' she asked Dendras when, for a short while, they were alone, Vidas having left them as they all moved from the restaurant to the lounge where the coffee was being served.

'He had some business to do in London and decided to fly up here to see me. At least, that's what he said.'

'Why did you let him believe we were serious?'

'I was flustered when I saw him there, at the university, in my room, and it seemed silly to tell him I was dining with a girl who'd thrown me over, especially as it was the girl I'd hoped to marry. So I let him believe it was serious.'

'And how are you intending to get out of it?'

'I'll have to think—' He stopped as Vidas rejoined them and sat down, his every movement as lithe as a jungle cat's, his features set, carved in the way that the forces of nature carve rock. Strange, unfathomable man, thought Kim. Did he ever unbend? Was he human?

It was a relief when the time came for them to leave the hotel. Dendras, looking exceedingly unhappy, bade her a rather stiff good night when, after he and Vidas

24

had walked with her to her car, he stood for a moment looking at her in the light from the hotel. 'When shall I see you again?'

'I'll give you a ring,' she promised, and after unlocking the door and sliding behind the wheel, was soon driving away, a sigh of relief on her lips.

Chapter Two

Her parents were still up when she arrived home, a circumstance which instantly set Kim wondering if something was wrong. They were in the habit of retiring early ever since her father was stricken with the heart attack that left him in such bad health that he had been forced to give up his work. Before that they had been comfortably off—Kim, her parents, and Stephen, a cousin whom her parents had adopted when his own parents were killed in a car accident. A year younger than Kim, he was something of a worry to them all. He had recently fallen in with a bad crowd and at times would not come home at night; on one occasion he was away for three days, and when questioned, refused to say where he had been.

The moment she entered the living room, Kim knew her fears were well founded, for her mother's eyes were swollen from weeping and her father lay on the couch, his face mottled, his lips ominously tinged with a blue that matched the knotted veins at his temples.

'What's wrong?' Kim's voice quivered, and in her heart there was dread. 'Father's had another attack?'

Her mother nodded. How old she looked these days, thought Kim sadly. And yet she was only in her early fifties, so she ought not to be looking as if she were ten years older.

'Yes, and the doctor says that if he has another, it could be fatal.' Kim frowned heavily as her glance slid from one parent to the other. 'It's all right,' her mother said. 'Your father knows the worst. He insisted that the doctor be frank with him.' A small pause followed, and then, 'Stephen's caused it—oh, Kim, he's done a *terrible* thing! And it looks as if the police will soon catch him even though he's in hiding.'

'In hiding?' Kim faltered, shock widening her eyes. 'What has he done?'

'It was robbery with violence—' She stopped, choked by sobs rising from the very depths of her being. Kim went to her swiftly, encircling her shuddering body with strong young arms. She herself was crying, her eyes on her father's inert figure on the couch. Anger forced its way through her pity and anxiety. To think that her parents had adopted Stephen only to be paid for their kindness in this way. She felt she hated her adopted brother with a black venom, and would be glad if he were caught and punished . . . glad if it were not for her parents and what his arrest would do to them. They had always been devoted to each other; theirs was the perfect example of what a happy marriage should be. They had been in love since the day they met, and they

27

would be in love until death parted them. Death . . .
She stared at her father and a great wave of despair
swept over her, for she could only fear the worst.

'Is there nothing that can be done?' She felt the
question to be superfluous but she had to say something. To her surprise she heard her mother say, in a
voice muffled against her breast, 'Your father thinks
that if only we could get away from here before the
arrest and trial—right away, he meant, so that the
disgrace wouldn't touch us—then he'd have a chance of
a few more years. You see, darling, we're respected
here, owing to your father's brilliant career as an
accountant, and we both know without any doubt at all
that the scandal would break us.'

'Move from here . . . ?' Kim eased her mother's
head away so that she could look at her. The tear-
stained face was more than she could bear, and for a
few tender moments she used her handkerchief to dry
her mother's eyes.

'Can we get away, darling?' her mother said and
there was a hopeless little catch to her voice. 'The
house had to be mortgaged when your father left work,
so we won't get much for ourselves if we do sell it.'

Another thing against moving was, of course, that
Kim would have to throw up her job, and as Stephen
had not been working for some time, her money was
the mainstay of the family.

'No, we can't get away,' her mother despairingly
said. 'We shall have to stay and face the scandal. . . .'
Her voice became muffled as she again pressed her face
to Kim's soft breast. But eventually she managed to
pull herself together and Kim suggested they all go to
bed. They would feel much fresher in the morning and
better able to discuss the situation to see if there was

any way in which the move could be made. Yet even as she spoke, hopelessness enveloped her, for it was impossible these days to make a move such as her mother suggested without money.

Kim lay awake far into the night, her thoughts flitting from one thing to another in her attempt to find a way of prolonging her father's life. Just before she had said good night, her mother had confided that, for some time now, her love for Stephen—and her husband's love for him—had been on the wane; immune to all pleading and distress, he had treated them diabolically, and the fact of his not working had increased their bitterness. It made Kim bitter too, since she had been forced to give up her spending money in order to help her mother to use as little as possible of their capital. Kim felt she would not care if she never saw Stephen again. She recalled vividly the words of an aunt—now dead—when Stephen was only ten years old.

'Your mum and dad made a bad move when they took that boy into their home, Kim. He'll bring them heartache aplenty—just you mark my words.'

She rose at dawn, having slept only fitfully after several hours of wakefulness. She moved about the house in silence, tidying up after making herself some tea. She had not even bothered to comb her hair, and at half past eight when she happened to glance in the mirror over the sink, she frowned darkly at her appearance. In addition to her hair being all awry, she had black rings under her eyes and her face was drawn and pallid; even her lips were colourless.

'I look ten years older than I am.' She sighed, and at that moment her ears caught the sound of a car turning into the short drive to the house. Her heart lurching at the idea of the police coming to say Stephen had been arrested, she hurried to the door, hoping to open it before the bell could ring. It was disgraceful of the police to come at this time—

'You!' she gasped, staring in disbelief at the man standing on the doorstep, his arrogant features cold and brittle. 'What do you want?' She shook her head in utter bewilderment. 'It's so early,' she added, feeling foolish, yet she had to say something.

'I know what time it is. But I have a plane to catch in just over two hours and I've things to say to you.' His eyes raked her body with icy distaste, and blushing hotly at the knowledge that her dressing gown was open at the front, revealing the transparent nightgown beneath it, she pulled the edges together and tied the cord. The hasty action brought a sardonic curve to his lips, and the sudden surge of hatred that swept through her knotted the muscles of her stomach. 'May I come in for a few minutes? As I said, there are things I want to talk to you about.'

Automatically, she drew the door wider, her thoughts switching to the couple upstairs, and she prayed that they would sleep for a little while longer. He came straight to the point once they were in the living room.

'You're to give my brother up,' he said harshly. 'I'm familiar with your type. You're just another gold digger who thinks she has a fool to deal with. As Dendras's guardian and protector of his fortune I have no intention of allowing him to marry you, so you can put the idea right out of your head!' He was standing in the middle of the room, a towering, menacing figure whose whole attitude was one of unmitigated contempt. 'I know I gave my consent, because of the information he offered me, but after meeting you I have changed my mind.'

Fighting for control, and at the same time infinitely curious, she said tersely, 'This information . . . er . . . what exactly did Dendras say to you?'

The dark eyes raked her with the same contempt as before. 'You know what he said! But I have changed my mind in spite of it. There will be no marriage between you and my brother!'

Kim let out an explosive breath, forgetting her curiosity as sheer fury took full possession of her mind. Yet, strangely, her voice was quiet and controlled as she said, 'You're so sure that my aim is to marry Dendras, but—'

'I have very little time at my disposal,' he cut in, glancing at his watch. 'All I've come here to say is that you can *forget* about marrying my brother!'

Kim's teeth snapped together. She had been on the point of telling him that she had no intention whatsoever of marrying his brother, but his arrogance, his air of superiority, and the contempt he made no effort to hide—all these combined to create an irresistible desire to keep him in suspense. She calmly reminded him that in a few month's time Dendras would be able to please himself, as he would have come of age. Almost immediately, though, she regretted her words and yet, paradoxically, she knew a tinge of satisfaction at hearing him grit his teeth in frustration.

'You are years older than he,' stated Vidas, his eyes searing her face as if he would create lines that were not there. 'I want your promise that you will leave my brother alone. He has his studies to think about—'

'Am I to understand,' broke in Kim quietly, 'that there have been other . . . er . . . gold diggers who have had ideas about marrying Dendras?'

'Several! And he always thinks he is madly in love!' A sneer caught his underlip, a sure indication of what he thought about love! 'I must admit, in all fairness, that you seem to be a little different from the others.' There was a frown between his eyes as he subjected her to a most searching scrutiny. 'Perhaps you have something to say in your defence?'

Now, of course, would be the time to confess that she had never had any intention of marrying his brother— or it would have been the time if he had not included those words '—in your own defence.'

Somehow they ignited a fierce and overriding increase in her animosity towards him, and instead of putting his mind at rest she found herself saying, 'No, Mr. Christou, I have nothing to say "in my defence," as you care to put it. I live my own life and take orders from no one. I am sorry to disappoint you—'

'You're determined to marry him?' White-hot fury robbed his face of its healthy tan. Kim watched the threatening clenching and unclenching of his lean brown fingers and knew without any doubt at all that he would love to have them round her throat. 'Woman, you will live to rue the day you set my authority at nought!'

Although trembling from head to foot, Kim managed to retain an outward calm, her voice surprisingly steady as, glancing at her wristwatch, she said, 'I must ask you to leave, Mr. Christou. You will appreciate that this is a most inopportune time for me to be dallying with visitors.'

She saw his eyes smoulder, his thin nostrils flare, and

then, without another word, he turned, and before she could precede him to the door, he was gone, leaving it wide open behind him.

Kim stood there motionless for a long time after he left. She was endeavouring to assess her feelings, for while on the one hand she felt nothing but dislike for the man, she was at the same time vitally aware of an odd sensation of gloom at the idea that he regarded her with such unmitigated scorn. It suddenly occurred to her that she was standing motionless, in a trancelike pose, her mind wholly occupied with the insufferable Vidas Christou. She had other, more important matters to which she ought to be giving her full attention!

The morning passed slowly, while Kim and her parents talked about the possibility of their leaving the district.

'Your father and I would have gone to a warmer, sunnier part of the world a long time ago if it hadn't been for you and Stephen,' Mrs. Rosswell admitted in an unguarded moment of stress. 'But although we decided we could let Stephen fend for himself, we couldn't leave you, Kim, and now it's too late. Our money won't stretch far enough.'

'I could have managed,' protested Kim in a pained little voice. 'Oh, Mother, why didn't you tell me what you and Father would have liked to do?'

'It's not important now, love,' interposed her father gently. He seemed to have recovered miraculously, being very much better than when Kim had seen him last night. 'I believe in fate, myself, and if it's meant that your mother and I are to find peace and contentment in our old age, then we shall certainly do so. Otherwise . . .' His voice trailed off to a significant silence and Kim turned away, an involuntary shudder passing through her body. She found herself dwelling on what Dendras had said about fate, and now her father had mentioned it as well. Kim found the word hammering in her brain, and for some incomprehensible reason her thoughts insisted that the two occurrences were inextricably linked.

Lunchtime arrived and still nothing had come of the discussions.

'There isn't any way we could raise sufficient money for a move,' Mrs. Rosswell said bleakly, as Kim rose from her chair to begin preparing the meal. She and her father had mentioned their having thought of living in Spain because several of their friends were retired there. It seemed that in some parts a community of English people had settled and Mr. and Mrs. Rosswell felt they could have adapted quite easily, but it seemed as if it was not to be.

'The apartments which some of our friends bought a few years ago have trebled in price.' Mr. Rosswell sighed. 'And so I can't see us ever being able to get away from here. Besides, if we're to escape the scandal, then it would have to be in the very near future.'

Kim went to the kitchen, her heart heavy. For her father was right. If the move were to be effective, then it must take place quickly, and not by any stretch of the imagination could Kim see this happening.

Dendras dead! Shocked and trembling, Kim stared at the tall foreigner who had brought the news, the man who, only a week before, had ordered her to give his brother up.

'It—it seems impossible.' She faltered, thinking of the utter waste of a young life. 'It ran onto the

pavement, you said? The lorry, I mean.' She scarcely
knew what she was saying, so heavy was her heart. It
was said that troubles never came singly, and how true
that was! Yesterday afternoon the police had called
again, and her father, though bearing up while they
were there, had broken down and gone straight to bed
when they left.

'Yes.' Vidas's mouth was tight, his handsome face
twisted in pain. 'So young.' He paused, looking at her.
It was Sunday, and she had washed her hair and set it.
She had determinedly made herself don something
smart and colourful, hoping to encourage her mother
to make an effort with her own appearance, for she was
letting herself go, oppressed with misery as she had
been this past week. Kim had succeeded in her objective, for her mother had put on a blue linen suit and
taken her husband for a stroll in the park. 'I thought I
would call and tell you in person rather than using the
telephone.'

'It was good of you,' she murmured, wanting to
assure him that she had never intended to marry his
brother, but aware that this was scarcely the time for
such an admission. It did not matter anyway, since she
would never be seeing this man again, or so she
thought. However, his next words were, 'You will want
to attend the funeral, I suppose?'

She bit her lip; attending a funeral at this time was
the last thing she wanted, but she supposed she ought
to do so. She wished she had been honest with Vidas at
first, and not let him believe that her relationship with
Dendras had gone deeper than mere friendship—at
least not on her part. However, there was nothing to be
done now and she agreed to attend the funeral.

'It's on Wednesday at ten o'clock in the morning.' He

gave her the full details and then left. And again she stood for a long while, silent and still, her mind confused, for this time new emotions had been stirred, emotions she had never experienced in her life before.

Kim did not tell her parents she was attending a funeral. She simply took time off from work, wishing more than ever that she did not have to go; she was sufficiently weighed down with worry already. Stephen had been arrested a few hours after Vidas's visit on Sunday, and the police had constantly been on the doorstep ever since; it seemed plain that they suspected her parents of receiving some of the ill-gotten gains. She must be passing through the blackest period she would ever experience in the whole of her life, Kim thought, for nothing could ever drag her spirits any lower than this.

Vidas met her outside the church. He seemed grimmer than ever, but there was another aspect about his demeanour that not only puzzled her but brought to mind the mystery—the mystery of what Dendras had said in order to get his brother's consent to the marriage—a marriage which in any case was destined never to take place.

After the funeral Vidas invited Kim to have lunch with him; she agreed, suspecting he would have insisted if she had refused. He obviously had something of vital importance to say to her, she realised, and in fact they had scarcely sat down at the table when he said, 'As you know, I am aware that you are pregnant, that you are expecting my brother's child.' So quiet and dispassionate the voice! Kim, the napkin she'd been about to shake out poised in trembling hands, could only gape at him, while the hot blood rushed into her cheeks.

'He—Dendras t-told you I—I . . .' Kim's voice trailed off into an incredulous silence as, in a flash, so much that had previously puzzled her was explained.

'Yes,' came the grim voice again. 'He told me about your condition—but we waste words since you already know that. Last Sunday I called with the intention of offering you a sum of money to give Dendras up, but your attitude was such that I lost my temper and walked out without making the offer.'

A light entered Kim's eyes. An idea was suddenly born. . . . She tried to put it from her but found herself saying, 'I suppose you are reconsidering, and will offer me money for—for the child—' Her nerves tightened and her throat went dry. What on earth was she about? How could she have intended, even for one moment, to rob this man? Unspeakably disgusted with herself, she tried desperately to reject the idea, but it persisted like the echo of a dream, recurring over and over again until it became an obsession, inextricably linked to her parents' plight. Rising before her was their miserable situation, and the added misery they would shortly endure when Stephen's trial came up. The disgrace would in all probability put an end to her father's life, and Kim suspected that her mother would not live long after him. She lifted troubled eyes to the man opposite her, a man of such great wealth he would never miss the sum of money required for the peace and happiness of her parents. And yet, her idea was too dishonest, too unscrupulous. Why, she could never live with her conscience!

But could she live with her conscience if she allowed her mother and father to suffer when she had it in her power to save them that suffering? Torn apart by the confusion, she put a trembling hand to her stomach, for she felt physically sick. Vidas, watching her closely, noticed the action, noticed too the ghastly pallor of her face. His eyes narrowed. She had the impression that there was pity somewhere behind that inscrutable stare, yet on the surface she saw only an implacable hardness, a total lack of compassion. Perhaps it was this that made her say, in tones husky and low, 'The settlement—what will it . . . amount to?'

'I am not now offering you money,' he returned, taking the menu from the waiter. 'In my family there is a tradition whereby, in a case such as yours, another member of the family will offer marriage, in order to give the child a name, and in this case an heir will be ensured as well.'

'In th-this case?' Kim quivered, her mind dazed by the situation in which she found herself. Clear thought was practically impossible, but she had to speak.

'I happen to be the only eligible male.' Coolly, he opened the menu and began to look through it, just as if his last words had been no more than a casual remark about something of little or no importance. The man must be insensible! He had no feelings; emotion seemed to be totally absent from his makeup.

'You are?' was all she could find to say as she sought for a handkerchief to wipe the perspiration from her forehead and the palms of her hands.

'I am offering you marriage,' he said, pausing from his survey of the fare to glance at her over the menu. 'It is the custom; also, marriage to you happens to suit a purpose I have in mind.'

'A purpose?' She suspected she knew what it was, but again she had to say something. 'And what is that?'

'It need not trouble you. Have you decided what you are going to eat?'

'I haven't seen a menu. In any case, I'm not hungry.'

The dark Greek eyes fixed hers. 'You need to eat,' he said authoritatively. 'We want a robust, healthy child.'

And I want to laugh, she thought—to laugh out loud in order to relieve this feeling of hysteria. Instead, she said, in tones amazingly steady, 'I have no wish to marry you, Mr. Christou, but the money would come in very useful at this time . . . because I shall have to give up my job.' What was she doing! This was not like her at all! Where was her honour? Why had she not been open with this man before now?

Fate . . . The word hammered in her brain, and alongside it the fact that she held an ace in her hand. Why should she not use it for the benefit of her parents?

'It is marriage,' she heard Vidas say through the chaos of her mind, 'or nothing. I am not now willing to offer you money.' Implacable the tone, forbidding argument.

'If I do agree to marry you, then I would want a settlement as well.' Slowly, the request came and she thought afterwards that some force over which she had no control was shaping all her words and actions. She did not even stop to think what marriage to this man would mean, what her life would be like or how her whole future would be affected. All she knew was that she must persuade him to give her money. And then, without warning, her brain cleared and the important fact leapt out at her. If she did marry Vidas, she would have to explain, in the near future, that she was not having a child. Her eyes darted to his. He would murder her, she thought, her glance now on his hands. Yes, he would slowly crush the life out of her with those slender fingers about her throat. She shuddered involuntarily as she accepted the menu he passed over to her.

'There will be no settlement. I am offering you marriage, with the benefits of a home and the status of a wife. That is all. I am offering you neither money nor a normal marriage.'

'I must have money!'

'Nothing doing. What sort of a fool do you think I am?'

Kim gritted her teeth at the insult. 'You don't trust me?'

'Correct. It's marriage or nothing.' In spite of the implacability of his words, Kim had the impression that he was disappointed at the way things were going, and this was perfectly understandable if, as she surmised, he wanted to rid himself of his stepmother. She said, watching him closely for any relaxing of that stony, inexorable expression, 'Then it's nothing.'

'Those are your last words?'

'Yes, Mr. Christou, they are my last words.' If he was disappointed so was she. For one triumphant interlude she had believed she held the passport to her parents' happiness in her hand, but now she was right back where she started from—a position of helplessness and despair.

Chapter Three

During the next few days Kim watched her father's
condition deteriorate as tension and anxiety built up;
she saw her mother become thin and ashen-faced as she
and her husband lost all hope of ever finding peace of
mind again. And in her frustration at not being able to
help, it was only natural that Kim's mind should
repeatedly recapture that meeting with Vidas Christou
when he had offered marriage but would not hear of a
monetary gift as well. If only there was a way in which
she could persuade him to change his mind. He had
been adamant about genuinely wanting her to accept
his offer even though he had not wanted her to marry
Dendras. The more she dwelt on it, the more attractive
the idea of writing to him and telling him the reason for
her wanting money became. Perhaps she would touch
some cord of compassion hidden in his Greek nature.
At last, having made a firm decision, she went up to her

room and took from a drawer the calling card given her by Dendras. The address was short and impressive: Castello Astura, Malindos, Greece.

As she wrote her letter she naturally thought about her 'condition' and tried to visualise what would happen when she said there had been a mistake and she was not pregnant after all. Would he accept her word, or would he decide she was a fraud? After thinking about it more deeply than she had before, Kim felt he would take her word, simply because Dendras had already conditioned Vidas's mind to the fact that she had genuinely believed she was pregnant. The next move on Vidas's part would surely be the request for an annulment, which would suit Kim very well, although this might be delayed if it so happened that Mrs. Christou had not yet made her departure from the castle. Yes, mused Kim as she continued to write, it was in the cards that Vidas would want an annulment, especially since the marriage was a sham anyway.

The answer to her letter arrived with surprising speed. Her mother glanced at the foreign stamp and asked who was writing to her.

'The Greek friend I told you about,' answered Kim, taking the envelope with a shaking hand.

'Oh, yes, I remember.' That was all. Mrs. Rosswell left her and went to give her husband his tablets and a drink.

Kim took the letter to her bedroom, holding it as if it were hot, her rather dazed eyes scanning the firm, strong handwriting. 'Imperious' and 'superior' were the adjectives that came to mind as she slit open the envelope, and it was only as she read the contents of the letter that she fully realised just how little hope she had had in her approach, how she had expected nothing to come of it. Yet what she read, on the contrary, was that Vidas was coming over to see her within the next day or so. Which is precisely what he did.

The interview, however, threatened to end abruptly when—as if the idea had only just occurred to him—Vidas asked if Kim was quite sure it was his brother's child she was expecting. At these words fire leapt to her eyes. If she still felt any guilt about the deception, those insulting and unnecessary words would have swept it away.

'Certainly it's his!' Kim felt as if she was not acting a part at all, but living through a real experience. 'How dare you ask a question like that?'

He looked down at her from his superior height, subjecting her to a long unnerving stare. She coloured with guilt and hoped he would take it for embarrassment.

'How old are you?' he demanded. 'Not as old as I at first assumed.'

'I'm almost twenty-three,' she answered, thinking it would not be surprising if she did look older, considering what she had been through during these past fateful weeks.

'How long did you . . . keep company with my brother?'

Kim licked her lips, sure of making a blunder whether she lied or not. She decided to tell the truth. 'Three months.'

'Three months, and you conceived a child.' Although there was nothing in his voice to betray his contempt, she knew it was there and she averted her eyes, swallowing convulsively. It seemed impossible that she should be emotionally affected by this man's contempt, and yet there was a strange, unbearable pain in the

43

region of her heart, as if a dagger were piercing it. She lifted her eyes to his, limpid eyes misted with tears, appealing eyes, which seemed to startle him and fix his gaze, and the long moment of silence became profound, electric. Kim felt prickles along her spine, and all at once her legs were weak and she swayed towards him. He put out his hands to steady her, warm strong hands that sent vibrations through her body. She closed her eyes, conscious of a sensation of nausea, and realised that the terrible strain of the past few weeks was beginning to have its affect on her.

'I—I must sit down,' she stammered, unaware that every vestige of colour had left her face.

'You're feeling ill?' Although there was harshness in his voice, she detected concern as well. 'Can I get you something?'

Her mouth felt painfully dry. 'A glass of water, please.'

He led her to the couch and sat her down, his gaze unreadable as she sank into the cushions and rested her head against the back of the couch.

'That's the kitchen?' He walked towards the door as he spoke. Kim wondered if he had ever seen the inside of a kitchen before. Certainly he had not been in a kitchen of such small dimensions.

He soon returned and she gratefully accepted the glass and its sparkling contents. Their fingers touched; she lowered her lashes to hide her expression.

'Thank you.' She put the empty glass into his extended hand after gulping down the water. 'I don't know what came over me.' She was thankful her parents were out walking in the park, her mother having decided to take advantage of the burst of sunshine that had dispersed the greyness of a cloud-filled sky. 'I don't often feel faint like that.'

'It's your condition, of course.'

Her condition . . . She had forgotten all about her pose! 'Yes, it must be,' she agreed weakly.

'You had better explain more fully why you want this money,' he said, getting down to business at last.

'You'll agree to my terms, then?'

'I do not care for the word "terms,"' he said, eyes glinting.

'I'm sorry. What I meant was—will you give me the money I need?'

'It depends on how much it is, and on whether I'm convinced by the story you tell me. There was enough in your letter to interest me, but certainly not to induce me to part with money unless I feel sure it's for the purpose you state.' He looked into her pale face and seemed deeply interested in what she would say.

'As I mentioned in my letter, my parents are in distress at the present time.' She went on to tell him of the scandal that would result from the trial, and the gossip that would continue afterwards. The disgrace, the shame, and the avoidance of contact with friends and neighbors. 'They must get away before it all begins,' she went on desperately. 'Then they will have a chance, at least, of happiness. I told you in my letter about Father's heart condition, didn't I?' She lifted her eyes to look appealingly at him and had the odd sensation of being examined for something he had missed. 'If he should have another attack he could die. . . .' Her voice weakened, then stopped, and two great tears rolled down her cheeks. 'I love my parents,' she whispered. 'And Mother's so in love with my father

that if he died then she—she would die too.' Her voice
caught and a strange, unfathomable expression crossed
the Greek's dark face.

'So they need money to get away from here?'

'Yes. The house is mortgaged.'

'I see. . . .' A thoughtful silence followed and then,
'Where do they want to go?'

Kim stared, searching his face. Although it was as
cold and hard as tempered steel, she found her heart
beginning to beat rapidly as hope gained strength
within her. 'Mother's mentioned Spain,' she answered
tentatively, 'as some of their friends have retired there.'

'They'd need to buy a house?'

'No, just an apartment.'

Vidas moved and stood with his back to the empty
fireplace, one hand thrust into his pocket, the other
fingering his chin thoughtfully. 'If you marry me I am
willing to supply the money for this apartment you
mention,' he offered at last.

'Oh . . .' The relief was overwhelming. 'Thank you
so very much.'

'I mentioned that the marriage will be in name only?'

'Of course.' She saw his mouth curve sardonically
and realised her colour must have mounted.

'I have no inclination to become emotionally involved either with you or any other woman.'

Kim's head jerked. What a way to talk! Still, as this
was a hardheaded bargain on both sides, plain speech
could not come amiss. 'I shall be free, then, to lead my
own life?' Quite naturally, she had forgotten what kind
of a woman she was supposed to be, but the expression
that entered his eyes soon reminded her even before he
spoke.

'You'll live a chaste life! The change will probably

take some getting used to, but, should you do anything to bring one breath of scandal to my name, you'll regret it with every hair of your head!'

'I shan't be bringing any scandal to your name,' she assured him tautly.

'You will remember, too, that my word is law in my own house.'

She said nothing. It would ruin her plan were she to allow her temper full reign at this moment, yet she was simply boiling inside. 'So it's settled, then?' was all she said. The sacrifice was going to be great, but she had no regrets and never would have, no matter what she went through as the wife of Vidas Christou. Her parents' happiness was ensured, and Kim knew a sort of serene resignation towards the part she was to play and the problems she might face before, her confession made, she would be free to leave her husband. And if he should consider himself to have been cheated, then she would pay him back, every penny, no matter how long it took.

'It's settled as far as I am concerned,' he said, breaking into her thoughts.

'You trust me, then? You didn't before.'

'Because I didn't know the money you wanted was for a genuine cause.'

'I could be deceiving you even now.'

'I shall want to meet your parents, naturally,' was his suave and pointed rejoinder. 'Do they know of your condition?'

'I didn't tell them.'

'You spared them the added anxiety?'

'Of course.'

'When can I meet them?'

'This evening, if you like.'

'That will suit admirably.' A smile touched his mouth and Kim stared in fascination. Her pulses were doing strange things, affected as she was by the sheer attractiveness of him, which she had felt now on more than one occasion. She wondered at the reason, since she so intensely disliked the man. 'Aren't your parents going to think it strange when you spring this on them without warning?'

'I've already thought of that. But they knew I was going out with a Greek, and as I never mentioned Dendras's age nor his name, they will naturally believe that you are him.'

His eyes flickered as he asked, 'Didn't you tell them that he was killed?'

'They had enough troubles without worrying unnecessarily about me.'

'You puzzle me,' admitted Vidas after a pause. 'Are you as bad as you appeared, I wonder?'

'I can love my parents and still be the—no-good you have branded me.'

The dark eyes glinted as they swept over her. 'Let me warn you, Kim, that no woman has ever laughed at me. If you are laughing at some joke of your own, then be very careful. My temper's always been unpredictable.'

She said nothing, and after a moment he seemed to forget his little spurt of anger and brought forward the question of their marriage. It would have to be in Malindos, he said, because he could not stay in England for more than a few days at the most.

'Mother will be disappointed.' Kim suddenly felt the prick of tears behind her eyes but valiantly fought them back, determined to think only of her parents and how they would soon be able to get away, into the sunshine, where they would find peace of mind.

'There's one thing,' Vidas was saying. 'I want every-one to believe the child is mine.'

'Everyone?' She stared uncomprehendingly. 'You have many in your family? Dendras said—'

'We have no relatives other than distant ones. I was referring to people in general and to my stepmother in particular. On no account must she ever guess that the child is not mine, understand?'

'Yes, I understand.' She had an almost uncontrolla-ble desire to laugh, simply because there was no child and never would be. In order to regain some modicum of sanity, she forced herself to talk about her parents and the move they would soon be making. 'I do sincerely thank you. It's—it's generous—' In spite of everything she broke down and wept. But almost instantly she was apologising, offering the strain of the past weeks as an excuse.

'It could be strain, partly,' he agreed, 'but I should say it's more likely to be your condition. I believe women can become exceedingly depressed when they are pregnant.'

What had she done? The enormity of it dropped like a ton weight on her shoulders. What would be the end of it all? What was Vidas's stepmother going to think—and say? How could she, Kim, carry off the added deception when the time arrived for her to tell her husband it had been a false alarm? Still, there were many bridges to cross before then, she thought grimly, resigned to gathering some scars along the way.

In spite of her confident words to Vidas she did, in fact, expect to encounter difficulties when she told her mother she was getting married. To her surprise and relief, the task proved much simpler than she would ever have imagined. The plain fact was that with so much happening in such a short time, Mrs. Rosswell's mind had become receptive to anything. Naturally she expressed surprise at first, but went on to say that her romance with Kim's father had developed just as suddenly and unexpectedly.

'We were married within two months of our first meeting,' she had more than once told Kim.

'You mentioned the young man but I didn't get the impression that it was serious,' said Mrs. Rosswell, after Kim had done a little more explaining. 'Will you like being married to a foreigner?' she asked. 'And living on an island? It's going to be such a change for you, darling.'

'I know, but I think it is all very wonderful.' Kim acted her part by producing a happy smile.

Had her mother not had such a weight on her mind, she would undoubtedly have shown more interest, but as it was, she merely expressed satisfaction that Kim at least would be away when the scandal broke, in the very near future.

'But you and Father are to be out of it too,' stated Kim, and went on to explain everything. 'Vidas wanted to help,' she went on, still acting her part. 'I said you'd like to go to Spain and he readily offered to buy you an apartment.'

At that, Mrs. Rosswell did show interest, gaping at her daughter as if she dared not believe her own ears. It couldn't be true, she murmured, but Kim assured her that it was.

'Vidas is a very wealthy man, Mother, and he'll never miss the money. He—he is doing it because he—he wants to make me happy.'

'Well, it's still unbelievable,' declared Mrs. Rosswell,

too excited to notice that her daughter studiedly avoided her gaze. 'Should I phone my friend and ask if your father and I can go over to stay with her until we find an apartment?'

'Of course. Vidas has made a promise and he can be relied upon to keep it. He's coming to see you both this evening.'

'It's like a miracle!' Mrs. Rosswell exclaimed a short while later as she came away from the phone. 'Marianne, my friend—you remember her?—says there is a very charming apartment in her block and it'll be vacant in a few days. It's for sale and she'll see the agent right away. Meanwhile, she says we can go over whenever we like!' Mrs. Rosswell hugged her daughter, tears dimming her eyes. 'My love, what a dramatic change in our circumstances! And all because you fell in love. Dearest, my one wish is that you will be as happy with your husband as I have been with mine!'

Kim looked away, her face pale; she hoped her mother would not notice her dejection. But she need not have worried; Mrs. Rosswell was so excited and absorbed in the prospect of peace of mind for her husband and herself that she did not even expect Kim to make any response. In fact, she changed the subject abruptly, saying that when the house was sold and the mortgage paid, the small amount left over would pay for any expenses incurred in setting up their new home in Spain.

'I think we shall buy all new furniture,' she declared. 'I'd like to sell almost everything and make a completely fresh start.'

'There's no reason why you shouldn't,' agreed Kim, feeling that her sacrifice had been worthwhile no matter what troubles might later come her way. 'You can leave it all to a house agent, Mother; there won't be any need for you to stay here much longer at all. In fact, it would be a good thing if you went while Father's feeling so much better.'

And it was, in fact, just four days later that Kim and Vidas took her parents to the airport in a taxi and said good-bye to them in the lounge.

'I only wish we could be at your wedding,' said Mrs. Rosswell regretfully. 'But the important thing is to get your father away and settled.' She lifted her face to look at Vidas, and it seemed to Kim that a timeless moment of sincerity passed as they stared into one another's eyes. That Vidas had been impressed by her parents was plain; that he wondered how they had come to have a daughter so lacking in morals and principles was also plain. 'We do thank you, Vidas,' Mrs. Rosswell said, then stopped to let her husband add his own words of gratitude. 'Make our little girl happy, won't you?' she begged finally and turned away, overcome by emotion.

Within an hour Kim and Vidas were back at her home, collecting her luggage, which was ready and standing in the hall. She glanced around, moved automatically to draw a curtain across one particularly sunny window, and then she turned and followed Vidas, securely latching the door behind her.

Kim stood before the long mirror of her dressing table, examining her pale face and wondering how she was going to extricate herself from the tangle of her deceit. She had been so obsessed by the idea of ensuring her parents' happiness and peace of mind that certain aspects of her situation had escaped her altogether . . . until a few minutes ago. Her husband had glanced fleetingly over her figure, and then said, in that urbane, foreign voice she had become used to since her marriage two weeks ago, 'It's time you saw our doctor. You'll need to be under his care from now on. I shall arrange it within the next day or so.'

Her heart lurched, almost seeming to spring from its moorings, and when she spoke, her voice shook with agitated tremors. 'Not yet, Vidas, surely? I feel absolutely fine, and I'm convinced there aren't going to be any complications.'

Breathlessly she waited, only to see him shake his head implacably and to hear him say, 'It's my wish that you be under medical care, Kim. Do not argue with me, understand?'

Meekly, she nodded, taking a deep breath in an attempt to still the agitation that continued to possess her. She felt that only a miracle could save her from some terrible form of retribution at her husband's hands.

'Yes, Vidas, I understand.' And she had made her escape, almost colliding with Alexandra, Dendras's mother, as she crossed the massive hall and reached the stairs. Alexandra had emerged from the salon to the left of the wide, balustraded stairway, the room being her boudoir, a sacred and inviolate sanctum, which Kim had not yet been permitted to enter.

'Running?' A frown and a lift of Alexandra's arrogant eyebrows followed the words. 'Take care! Remember you are carrying my stepson's child!'

What a woman! Fury left Kim visibly shaking. From the first moment they met, Kim had disliked her intensely. Black-eyed, cold, and distant, she was the most objectionable person Kim had ever had the misfortune to meet. As she had shown no sign of sorrow at her son's death, Kim guessed that if grief did affect her, she would rather die than show it. Her dignity was almost frightening, her acid tongue an instrument whose sting had already discouraged Kim from entering into conversation if it were at all possible to avoid.

As for Vidas's attitude—it was a little better, but he too could be icily cutting at times. Kim had been left in no doubt, right from the start, that she was regarded with contempt for what she had done—or was supposed to have done—and also for what she was: an inferior. Yes, she was unmistakably treated as an inferior, but for all that, she had been accepted, because she was to provide an heir to the Christou wealth.

What a plight she was in! She almost wished she *were* having Dendras's child. It would certainly solve all her problems! If only she had made her admission *before* Vidas mentioned the doctor. Although she tried to muster up the courage on a couple of occasions, she had shirked the ordeal, and to do it now must look so suspicious that Vidas would be sure to accuse her of having been lying in the first place. Feeling totally unable to cope with the problem, she actually succeeded in thrusting it temporarily from her mind, and moving away from the large, gilt-embellished dressing table, she went to the wardrobe to look for a suitable gown for this evening. Vidas had brought a dressmaker up to the castle and Kim had been measured for dresses, skirts, and blouses. No slacks. She would not be wearing slacks, Vidas had stated, and she did not trouble to ask whether this rule held permanently or just while she was in her present 'condition.'

After making her choice, she laid the dress on the bed, her pensive gaze fixed on the high, richly carved door, the door that led into her husband's suite of sitting room, bedroom, dressing room and bathroom. She had been in it once, venturing a quick look when she knew that Vidas was not in the house. Like her own suite, it possessed the mellowed quality that pervaded the whole vast edifice. The walls were hung with tapestries; the drapes were rich crimson Italian brocatelle; the thickly luxurious carpets spread from wall to wall. The high ceiling of the sitting room was of a geometric design, lavishly embellished with gold leaf; the white marble fireplace flaunted the arms of an illustrious Italian house, testimony to its origin in some mansion that particular family once owned. There was a superb writing table set in the deep window, its matching *cartonnier* close by. The black lacquer bookcase was filled with leather-bound volumes—priceless editions, Kim surmised. The rest of the elegant furnishings were all antique, the two tables gleaming with the patina of age, the sofa and chairs upholstered in French tapestry, multicoloured but subdued.

As it was too early to bathe and change, she decided to go for a walk on the beach, a favourite place since the day she discovered the lonely cove backed by palms and plane trees, which provided welcome shade from the fierce Grecian sun. Here she could relax, away from the castle and the people in it; here she could be alone with her thoughts.

Chapter Four

Reaching the cove, Kim stood looking out over the golden-blue of a sun-spangled sea, watching its slow rise and fall, noticing a white-sailed yacht riding in graceful motion against an egg-shell sky. The salt tang drifted in on the zephyr of a breeze, and the movement of the water made slender curls of blue-white froth roll gently in towards the shore. Behind her the breeze rustled the foliage of the trees, and the incessant trill of cicadas floated on the air. In the undergrowth corn poppies of brilliant scarlet mingled with the delicate gold gold of crown daisies and the mauve-blue of borage. So much variaion of form and colour! Its beauty took Kim's breath away and for a few treasured moments her mind became free of all anxieties and doubts. She swung round to absorb the entire aspect in all its sun-gold of old glory——the waving palms, the polished leaves

of carob trees, the olives against the hillsides, a tantalising silver at one moment, pewter-grey the next. High
in the heavens filmy trails of cirrus clouds streaked
the blue, drifting and swirling in fascinating shapes.

Strangely, considering the weight of her problem,
her spirits lifted as she stood there, a lone figure on the
seashore, her ears attuned to the variety of sound, her
eyes appreciative of the variety of form.

The minutes stretched to more than an hour, and it
was only when a restlessness assailed her that she
decided to return to the castle. And immediately with
this decision came the pressing weight of her problem,
the magnitude of her offence hovering within her mind,
a smothering cloud ruthlessly enveloping her until
there was no escape, no peace. What had seemed so
simple at the outset now seemed impossible. How
could she go to her husband and say she had made a
mistake, how confess that there was no child after all?
A few days ago she had toyed with the idea of saying
she'd had a miscarriage, but that was now impossible,
seeing that Vidas had been in touch with the doctor.
No, it had to be the original idea, but how to apply it
was something that Kim could not now visualise.

As she entered the grounds of the castle she saw her
husband. A wild, uncontrollable panic seized her and
she could think of only one course open to her: she
would write him a full confession, then flee, shaking the
soil of his country from her shoes forever. But no . . .
Aside from the pangs of conscience already assailing
her, there was the far more oppressive awareness that
Vidas would contact her parents. He knew their address and it was logical to assume that his first act would
be to get in touch with them, if only to find out where

their daughter was. Kim could visualise their concern, their happiness shattered at the breakup of her marriage.

'God help me,' she prayed. 'What must I do?'

Vidas had not seen her and she halted by a cluster of trees, her full attention fixed on his tall, athletic form. How handsome he was despite his austerity, how superlatively male! He was walking slowly along the edge of a border, hands loosely clasped behind his back, his dark head forward as if he were deep in thought, with all else escaping him. Kim was vitally aware of the gulf between them, created by his cold, indomitable withdrawal, his arrogant assumption of authority. In a way he reminded her of his stepmother, with her insufferable pride. Kim was ever conscious of the woman's contempt and the condescending way she was treated by her, and there were times when, goaded almost beyond endurance, she could almost have blurted out the truth: that she was not having a child at all. As yet Alexandra had made no move to leave the castle, but certain changes were taking place, changes insisted on by Vidas. Her place had been changed at the table; Kim now sat at the end facing her husband. Vidas also insisted that Kim gradually take over the management of the house, assuming authority over the servants. Alexandra bitterly resented these changes but could do nothing about them. Kim had done as she was told, even though she had no wish to usurp the older woman's position. On the contrary, she would have preferred to leave things as they were.

Vidas had still not noticed his wife, standing there in the shade of the trees, and her brooding eyes travelled from the noble forehead to the line where the thick hair met it, and higher to where the dark waves strayed backwards, and then to the silver threads shining at his temples. Truly a distinguished man, impressively superior, unapproachable. And yet, was he really as cold and distant as she had branded him?

During the fortnight she had been his wife, various facets of his personality had been revealed to her, through her own observations, since he certainly never volunteered anything about himself. But at times she encountered disturbing qualities about him that alerted her sensitive mind to danger. She became vitally aware of his dark eyes burning with a distinctly amorous light when they looked at her, and she would not have been a woman had she failed to recognise the signs, to accept the fact that she was beginning to interest him. Not spiritually; most certainly she appealed to what some people would term 'his baser instincts'—the sensual, passionate side of his nature. He was of the East and also of the race whose reputation for being preoccupied with sex was known the world over. So it was natural that she should regard his interest with some foreboding, dreading to think what the outcome might be; for if he should decide to put their marriage on a normal footing, she would be helpless to deny him his rights.

He half turned, after standing motionless and watching a slender little gecko catch insects with its long dark tongue. Kim stepped back, to blend further into the shadow of the trees. The reason for this action eluded her, but she seemed compelled by some force beyond her control to look at him, long and hard . . . and she found a strange, intangible pleasure in doing so! Pleasure? A frown creased her wide, intelligent forehead at the idea that had unwontedly come to her, stirring unconscious emotions, awakening her senses as the first rays of dawn awoke the earth to the vibrations of life. She was deeply moved without knowing why, and a tentative yearning touched her heart. From the dark recesses of her mind, words emerged with startling clarity: 'This man is my husband. He belongs to me, just as I belong to him.'

They had been married in the mellowed little church high on the valley side a short while after they arrived on Malindos by boat, having flown to Athens and then taken the ferry. They had passed other islands on the way, some so small as to be mere rocky summits of the vast volcanic mountain range that lay beneath the waters of the Aegean Sea. All had been so strange, and yet she had known excitement too, and a sense of adventure to mitigate the fear which hung over her when she thought of the stony path she might be called upon to tread.

For Kim the marriage ceremony was memorable in spite of the lack of guests and music and flowers and the sweet young voices of choir boys—how often she had formed the picture of a white wedding, with two hundred guests and all the trimmings! Yet, somehow, as she had stood with Vidas before the swarthy, long-bearded priest of the Greek Orthodox Church she had been touched in a way she would not have believed possible when first she contemplated marrying for the sole purpose of easing her parents' lot. It had been a business deal on her part, suited to her own ends, without a thought for the man she was duping. Because she had disliked him on sight, her act seemed not quite so iniquitous as it would have seemed had Vidas been a likeable man. But now . . . Gradually she had been learning to see her husband in a new light. He had faithfully played his part; even now her parents were preparing to move into their new home, and the

Spanish doctor who had her father under his care had confidently assured her mother that his condition would continue to improve.

Suddenly Vidas became aware of being watched and swung round, scanning the shadows until he spotted her. She coloured and came forth reluctantly, slowly walking towards him, a smile quivering on her lips. His long lithe body never moved; it was as if he considered it his right to have her come to him, and not he to her, and slowly her smile ebbed. As she drew close she was sure she heard him catch his breath. He stared at her in a long unsmiling appraisal before breaking the silence, which for Kim was fast becoming fraught with tension.

He said, 'Where have you been? Your mother phoned just now—'

'Mother!' In spite of the reassurance she had received by telephone three days ago, Kim's heart lurched as fear spread over her. 'Father's had another—?'

'He's fine,' broke in Vidas, as if to spare her any further anxiety. 'They're thoroughly enjoying their new life in the sunshine.'

'They've moved into their apartment?' Kim's relief showed as the lost colour flowed back into her cheeks. Vidas stared, an odd, frowning expression in his eyes. He seemed puzzled by her manner, and she was forcefully reminded of that other occasion when he had intimated that something about her baffled him. Could it be that his opinion of her was gradually changing? The idea brought a lightness to her spirits and she grasped the reason instantly. She desperately wanted him to like her, to be friendly towards her and treat her as an equal.

'They moved in yesterday, and all their friends and

neighbours have been helping, so it would seem that your parents are very fortunate.'

'It's all due to you.' Her voice was quiet, filled with gratitude. 'You've been so kind to them.' But not particularly kind to me, she added silently, then admitted at once that there was absolutely no reason why he should be kind to her. Their marriage meant nothing; it had taken place for no other purpose than to give a child its rightful name.

And there was no child. . . . This thought led quite naturally to the problem facing her, and she wisely decided that the confession would best be made as soon as an opportunity arose, for there was nothing to be gained by further delay. She would be a nervous wreck if she went on like this much longer. Besides, she would in any case have to confess within the next few days, owing to the appointment Vidas was making for her to see the doctor. If only she knew how Vidas would react, though. At times she was sure he would accept the new situation philosophically, but there were occasions of doubt, when fear would creep in; for if suspicion should enter his mind, and he should accuse her of fraud, she felt sure she would never be able to stand before him and deny it. The deceit had been difficult enough the first time; it would be impossible for her to repeat it.

He was speaking, commenting on her words about his kindness to her parents. 'It was my duty to help my wife's people.'

'I wasn't your wife at that time.'

'You were soon to become my wife.' His hooded eyes flickered over her figure and she felt her nerves tense. She supposed she should have lost her waist by now but instead it was as neat and trim as ever. 'I have phoned the doctor and he'll be calling the day after tomorrow at eleven o'clock in the morning. He believes the child is mine, of course.' Unemotional were the words and the manner of their delivery. It was Kim who was squirming with embarrassment.

'He knows when we were married.' She spoke automatically, the statement a natural follow-up to what Vidas had said.

'Of course.' A casual shrug preceded his next words. 'He will think, but certainly not comment.' The remote indifference of his tone was proof of his unconcern for the opinion of others . . . and yet he had warned her in no uncertain terms, that he would never tolerate scandal brought to his name by his wife. It was as if he himself were supreme, so arrogantly confident of that supremacy that he was like a king—above criticism.

'You can telephone your parents anytime you wish,' he was saying as they walked slowly towards the tower-flanked entrance to the castle. 'Your mother's given me a number. It's the phone number of the people in the adjacent apartment.'

'It's kind of their neighbours to let them use their phone.' Vidas was slightly ahead of her and, to her surprise, he slowed to match his pace to hers. Why her feet were dragging she could not say, but they were. The last hour had been rather wonderful, her burden temporarily lifted as she enjoyed her solitude, but now . . .

Her thoughts had returned to the possibility of his wanting to end the marriage and she realised that this was the source of her dejection. Staggered by the knowledge, which could not be denied, she was dazed for a moment as she tried to discover the reason for it. Why should she feel this desolation at the thought of leaving the castle and returning to her own country? After all, it was what she had wanted—an annulment and freedom again, even though her parents would be upset at the breaking up of the marriage. She had given this a great deal of thought and decided she could convince them that she wouldn't be hurt in any way—that she genuinely wanted a separation. But she now freely admitted that a separation was the very last thing she wanted. As she wandered along beside the tall figure of her husband Kim's mind became a whirlpool of questions, and as they were answered she shook her head, frantically trying to discard the one answer to which all the questions had led.

She could *not* be falling in love with her husband! It was impossible! He had never given her any encouragement; any conversation they had was impersonal, and almost always she would encounter a scathing glance to remind her of his opinion of her. Although she believed that opinion had improved a little, she was ever conscious that her 'condition' reminded him that she had been his brother's pillow-friend. If only he could know the falsity of that belief, but it wasn't possible to enlighten him under the present circumstances. In any case, he would never believe her even if it were possible, she admitted with a sigh. She sent him an upward glance as they neared the castle, its entrance looming before them, its noble façade clothed with luxuriant ivy. His body was erect, head set high on broad, arrogant shoulders. In profile he was attractive enough, but when he turned, conscious of her stare, she caught her breath as something quickened in her veins and she again found herself trying to deny that she was falling in love with him.

He glanced down and was puzzled by her expression.

'Something wrong?' The fine-drawn intentness of his eyes robbed her of confidence and her reply was stilted and awkward.

'No, nothing's wrong.' She caught a movement at one of the windows of the castle and stared. Alexandra's boudoir . . . The fine lace curtains fluttered and a dark shadow flitted away from the light. 'Your stepmother doesn't like me.' The words flowed swiftly, thoughts spoken aloud. 'Dendras didn't seem to get along very well with her, either—from what he told me.'

'Alexandra is old,' remarked Vidas, nothing in the accented voice to betray his inner thoughts. 'She is often impatient with youth. Dendras was not all she would have wished a son to be.' Vidas paused a moment, his glance fleeting as it swept his wife's figure. 'She had put all her hopes in his producing an heir.'

'She wanted Dendras to inherit everything?'

'Naturally. Throughout history this kind of thing has happened when a man has sons by different wives. The second wife invariably feels her son is being cheated.' Cold and unemotional was his voice. He stopped walking and Kim saw his eyes stray to Alexandra's window. He too was aware that they were being watched. 'You can now understand why I want her to believe the child is mine.'

'Spite?' The one brief word did nothing more than bring a sneer to his sensual mouth.

'Call it what you like. I shan't give her the satisfaction of knowing her grandchild will inherit all this.'

'But you, Vidas—surely you could have had an heir long ago? I mean, you could have married before now.'

'I could have done,' he agreed, 'but the inclination was not strong enough.'

'It seems strange that a man in your position did not want to produce his own heir—' She stopped abruptly, another rush of colour rising in her cheeks as she realised just how crudely she had phrased her words. Vidas's eyes seemed to be riveted on her, an odd expression in their depths.

'You sound genuinely concerned about my not having an heir,' he commented, and it seemed to Kim that his voice was tinged with asperity. He was puzzled by her manner, by the apparent sincerity of her concern. The dark eyes narrowed, examining her face intently in the silence. 'What kind of a woman are you?' he demanded. 'I once said I had the impression that you were laughing at me, and if so, it means you have a secret, that you know something which I do not.' Anger was in his tone now as well as impatience and the hint of a threat. 'I am beginning to think you are a deep one, my girl!' And without giving her the chance of speaking, he turned and strode away towards one of the rear entrances to the castle.

Kim stared after his swiftly retreating figure, her pulses racing as fear crept through her whole being. If ever he should discover the truth—that she had never slept with his brother, or with any other man for that matter! It did not bear thinking about and she determinedly refused to dwell upon it. Other thoughts, equally disturbing, filled her mind. This new emotion, this yearning . . . for what? It was useless to deny that her husband's attractions drew her physically, and she wondered if her desire was born merely of the newly awakened needs of the flesh, or if, as had already occurred to her, she was falling in love. What folly that would be! Disastrous! Because Vidas would never in a thousand years return that love. She must not let her mind dwell on it, because if she did she was lost. But already she knew she *was* lost. . . .

Dinner that evening was vastly different from usual, because Alexandra had decided to dine alone in her boudoir.

The sky had darkened soon after Kim had come in from the garden, presaging a storm, yet even though it broke, raging throughout the meal, the atmosphere within the room itself was clearer, brighter than usual, owing to the absence of Mrs. Christou. Having forgotten the little spurt of anger he had exhibited earlier, Vidas conversed more affably with his wife than ever before. If it had not been for her nagging worry over the confession she must soon make, Kim could have been profoundly happy sitting there, alone with her husband, dining by candlelight in the gracious salon that was part of the ancient banqueting hall of the castle.

It was when they were in the lounge, which was also part of the banqueting hall, drinking coffee and cognac, that Kim decided to get the whole thing over and done with. Yet her heart began to throb as soon as the resolve was made; her tongue became dry so that, when eventually she did manage to speak, her voice sounded strained and harsh even to her own ears.

'Vidas, I'm—I'm afraid I have—have a disappointment for you. . . .' She swallowed thickly, nerves jagged but resolution still strong, for it was impossible to endure this tension any longer; it had oppressed her since the moment Vidas had mentioned the doctor. 'It—it was all a mistake, Vidas—a—a false alarm.'

Silence followed, oppressive and intense. Kim wondered if she looked as white as she felt.

'What,' enquired her husband in a smooth urbane voice, 'was a false alarm?' The direct, unnerving stare was as cold as tempered steel. 'Well?' he murmured gently when she did not speak.

'I'm n-not having a—a baby after all.' There, it was out and she must accept the consequences. He would not murder her—or would he? Involuntarily a hand crept to her throat, as if she would protect it from any possible attack.

'When did you make this discovery?'

'Only today—th-this evening just before dinner.' The hand left her throat to move to her breast, beneath which her heart pounded in the most alarming way. 'I'm sorry for all the trouble, Vidas. It was silly of me to make a mistake like that.'

'But most convenient,' he commented, his face a dark, unreadable mask.

'I d-don't know what you mean, Vidas.' With trembling fingers Kim reached for her glass and put it to her lips, having to use all her control not to drink the fiery liquid in one swift gulp, because she felt she needed it.

'The mistake, as you term it, enabled you to provide for your parents' removal to Spain.'

Fear darkened her eyes. 'You don't think—I mean—surely you accept my word—that it was a genuine mistake on my part?'

'I have already said there's something about you that I can't fathom.'

'You must believe me!' she cried, heart pounding against her ribs. 'It's—it's the truth and so you *must* believe me!'

'And if I choose not to believe you?' His piercing gaze was inescapable; Kim felt like a helpless creature about to be attacked by a ruthless predator.

'Please believe me,' she begged, tears filling her eyes. 'Vidas . . . you're frightening m-me.' Although acutely aware that the manner she was adopting was in total variance with what she was supposed to be—worldly and confident, the experienced gold digger he had branded her, and a woman of loose morals as well— Kim could not control the plea in her voice, the visible trembling of her body, the tears falling on her cheeks. 'Mistakes like this are made all the time,' she went on desperately. 'You—you act as if—as if my case is unique.'

Vidas reached for his coffee cup, his narrowed eyes fixing hers from above the rim. 'Perhaps your particular case *is* unique,' was his soft and subtle rejoinder.

'I still d-don't know what you m-mean.' The glass in her hand was shaking and she put it down on the table with a little bang.

'Can you explain what made you so sure you were expecting my brother's child?' Vidas's voice cut a silence that had stretched Kim's nerves almost to the breaking point. In the sheer undiluted panic that winged through her, she felt she must either make a full confession or run from him, into the chill and patchy blackness of the rain-swept gardens, where she could lose herself in the enfolding safety until all danger had passed. It was a fanciful idea, untenable, and she drew a swift breath of relief when her husband's voice put an end to it.

'I took it for granted,' she managed, wishing her heart would not pound so agonisingly against her rib cage, that her pulse was not so erratic.

'You took it for granted, without seeing a doctor?' The lean dark face retained its inscrutable expression and the glacial, perfectly controlled voice was equally uncommunicative. 'Purely on that assumption you were pressing Dendras to marry you?'

'I did not press him,' she began indignantly.

'But you did. You were determined to marry him. Also, on the same assumption, you asked me for money.'

Kim licked her lips. 'I—I genuinely believed I was—was . . .' She could not go on. It was too much for her nervous system to endure. The truth was her only salvation . . . but what then? Surely Vidas would do her a physical injury on learning just how cleverly he had been duped.

'Perhaps you did genuinely believe you were pregnant,' came her husband's staggering concession at last. Kim stared, shaking her head as if to clear her thoughts.

'You do believe me, then?'

'You make it all sound very convincing.' Was there a cynical ring to his voice, she wondered, or had she imagined it?

'It was a natural conclusion, Vidas,' she said quietly but could not meet his eyes.

'Because you had slept with Dendras?'

'Of—of course,' Little beads of perspiration caused tendrils of hair to cling to her forehead. Kim brushed an unsteady hand across it, her eyes now fixed on those of her husband, not through her own willingness but through his. She felt the magnetism he was exerting over her, the supreme power that sapped what little strength she had left. However, he seemed, after a prolonged moment of thought, to adopt an attitude of resignation. He must have realised, decided Kim, that what was done was done, and there was nothing he could do to alter it.

'So there's to be no heir after all?'

'No—I am sorry.'

The dark Greek eyes flickered strangely. 'I wonder,' he said slowly. 'I wonder if you really are sorry.'

'I meant for the trouble I've caused.' He said nothing and after a moment she ventured the suggestion that he would be wanting an annulment. She was fast regaining her composure, scarcely able to credit her good fortune in escaping her husband's wrath.

'An annulment?' he repeated, eyebrows lifting a fraction. 'There'll be no annulment. We're married and that's the way it stays, at least for a time.'

'You still want me to remain here?'

'I not only want you to stay but I intend you to.'

'But—'

'What gave you the idea that I would want to end our marriage?' he broke in tersely.

'I took it for granted that, under the circumstances, you would want your freedom.'

'I am quite satisfied with things as they are.'

She said, watching him closely, 'Your stepmother should have left here on your marriage. You haven't yet told her to go.'

'Yes, I have. The arrangement provided by my father's will was that she be given a reasonable time to establish a home for herself. She'll be leaving within the next month or so.'

'I see.' Would Vidas then reconsider and want an annulment? 'Dendras told me all about the will. I guessed that you married me in order to make her leave your home.' Her voice was quite steady now, a result of her somewhat settled nerves, and she found herself able to speak more freely than usual. 'The marriage, Vidas, helped us both, didn't it?'

'As you say, it helped us both.'

'So, in spite of everything, I have been of some little use to you, haven't I?'

'Marriage to you has served a purpose, yes.' Vidas was holding his glass up to the light, watching the oily effect of the brandy on its gleaming sides. He seemed thoughtful, and when presently he spoke, it was to reveal what he had been turning over in his mind. 'As I have mentioned, marriage has never appealed to me; I can manage very well without the cloying female sentimentality and all it entails. So-called love has certainly never affected me,' he went on, and now Kim detected a sneering, cynical edge to his voice. His expression, too, was sardonic, and the vestige of a contemptuous smile played about his mouth. That he was ridiculing the romanticism of women was all too plain.

'From what I have seen, love is a transient emotion in any case, leaving nothing behind but acrimony and bitterness. No man with an atom of sanity would fall, open-eyed, into a net like that.' He paused to listen to the lash of rain on the windows. 'However, in spite of my distaste for marriage, I realised that if ever I were to rid myself of my stepmother I must either marry or wait until she died. She and I had been passing through a particularly unpleasant period when, by a quirk of fate, you and I met.'

'It proved to be opportune for you,' Kim could not help saying.

'It certainly was to my advantage,' he agreed. His eyes slid over her in a frowning glance. 'I had to give the matter a good deal of thought,' he went on reflectively. 'Greek men do not take kindly to females who give themselves away before marriage.'

'Yet, conversely, you have pillow-friends.' Kim's voice was tart, her composure almost normal.

To her surprise Vidas laughed. 'It might appear illogical to you, Kim, but it is just a way of life we have, which happens to differ from that of the West. Yes, we do have pillow-friends, yet we insist on a record of total chastity in the women we marry.' Kim shot him a glance, to which he promptly responded, his eyes filled with mocking amusement. 'I am speaking, of course, of a normal marriage.'

'Of course,' she said with a dry inflection. She could not help but be amused, although her amusement stemmed from a very different circumstance than her husband's. She wondered what he would say were she to tell him that she was, in fact, an eligible wife for a Greek, being possessed of total chastity as he had put it. However, she was now becoming used to the role of 'fallen woman,' as no doubt he described her to himself, for she had known from the first that she must become resigned. 'It seems to me that the women of your country have a raw deal whether they are chaste or not.'

'Oh, why?'

'They're subjugated.'

'No such thing. Women like to be mastered.'

'There's a difference between mastery and subjugation.'

'A narrow margin. However, it's of no importance either to you or me, since our marriage is a sham and always will be.'

A sham and always will be . . . How long could she go on living a life like that, her love growing stronger all the time? A shuddering sigh escaped her and she said tentatively, 'How long do you want us to stay married?'

'I have no idea yet. My stepmother could ask to come back if she became aware that the marriage had ended.'

'But would she—once she had left?'

'She might. It's a risk which I have no need to take. I want your promise that you will stay here until I decide otherwise.'

'If I refuse, you would, I suppose, get in touch with my mother?' She had no intention of refusing but she was interested in his reaction.

'Are you intimating that I would blackmail you?' he countered, his eyes hard as steel.

'No—er . . .'

'Be very careful in your attitude, Kim,' he warned softly. 'You haven't yet come in contact with my temper.'

'I didn't mean . . .' Again she stopped. 'I'm sorry,' she murmured after a pause. 'I give the promise, and shall keep it.'

Chapter Five

Another fortnight passed, with Kim taking over the running of the castle. It was a task which had scared her at first, until it became evident that Litsa, the housekeeper, whose activities had been curtailed by Alexandra, was only too eager to do the work for which she was paid, and so Kim found herself falling into the pleasant routine of merely discussing meals, seeing that supplies were ordered, and generally supervising whenever necessary. And as her confidence increased she began moving furniture around, including some of the priceless antiques. From the first she had been enchanted with a small, drably furnished room with a view of the immense expanse of sea—mauve and aquamarine with frothy whiteness curling indolently towards the shore. From another window she could see the other castle of which Dendras had spoken, owned by the Greek who had married the Irish girl. Kim thought she would like to meet this couple one day, but meanwhile, she began expending all her energies on making the small room into a cosy snug for her own private use. It was on the first floor, and also looked out over the beautiful grounds of the castle with their ever-changing moods and colours, affected as they were by light and shade, and by the clouds that often gathered and swirled in the sapphire vault of the heavens.

Kim had a happy time fixing up the snug, this in spite of the complaints of Alexandra, who, in no uncertain terms, told her that she ought not to be moving antique objects into this room, nor should she have removed two French armchairs from the blue and gold salon.

'The place will hardly be recognisable if you carry on like this much longer!' she exclaimed, but Kim merely ignored the complaints, more impatient with the woman's exaggeration than with her interference. When at length the snug was to her liking Kim invited her husband in to see it. He stood in the doorway, an unfathomable expression in his dark eyes. She smiled inwardly, knowing just how puzzled he was by her, and that his puzzlement was increasing all the time. By now he seemed to have accepted without question that she was not the vulgar, cheap little schemer he had at first believed her to be, but beyond that, he could not make her out at all. According to his idealistic Greek requirements for a woman she was sadly lacking, having given herself to his brother, but apart from her morals she was in fact a 'nice girl.' This was the impression Kim had gained recently and she was sure it was a correct one.

'Do you like it?' she asked with a smile when he made no immediate comment.

'It's charming, Kim—really cosy and welcoming.'

'It's meant to be welcoming,' she ventured, and there was no mistaking the significance of her words. Vidas moved into the room and sat down on the sofa.

'Well, aren't you going to offer me a drink?' he asked.

'I haven't anything.'

'Then we must rectify that. There's a small but very charming cocktail cabinet in Alexandra's boudoir. I'll have it fetched out and put in here—'

'Oh, no, please don't do that, Vidas,' Kim begged. 'I can wait until she has left.'

'If we strip her room, she'll leave much more quickly. The trouble is she's far too comfortable.'

'It's not nice to take things from her rooms.' The distress in her voice came through but had no effect, and the following day the cabinet was brought to the snug along with some bookshelves and a charming sofa table of the Georgian period. It had come from England, as had the cabinet. Then came a Chelsea-Derby group and a Sèvres vase. Kim told Vidas at dinner that night that she did not want anything else for the snug.

'You don't like Alexandra any more than I do,' he said with a frown, 'so why this objection to making her so uncomfortable that she'll leave?'

Kim said nothing else, but she had succeeded in putting a stop to the removal of items from the older woman's boudoir.

Ten days later Alexandra moved out of the castle, having managed to rent a villa at Hatla, close to the capital of the island, but she told Kim she would not settle there.

'I prefer a larger island,' she had added. 'Malindos has always been too small for me.'

Vidas was totally unmoved, not offering to help even on the day Alexandra actually left. As for Kim, she had eagerly looked forward to the departure of the woman whose deliberate and calculated offensiveness had sorely tried her patience on so many occasions. But now, after Alexandra had gone, she could not understand her continued restlessness. She ought to have been totally at ease, freed as she was from any further insults, yet there was a sort of brooding introversion about her as she paced her room that night. At last she owned that it was her feelings for her husband that disturbed her, the knowledge that her love would never be returned. By his own admission he had no intention of ever being affected by what he once described as a superficial emotion peculiar to women rather than men. But even if he were capable of loving, she would be the last one on whom he would be likely to centre his affection.

Kim sighed heavily, deciding to relax in the bath, even though she had showered before dinner. The warm scented water would be soothing, she thought. Yet when she came out, dried and powdered herself and donned a dainty diaphanous nightgown, she began again to experience the restlessness, and in addition she fell to brooding on her situation and the hopelessness of her love for her husband. Yet suddenly she wanted nothing more than to get away from the man who, all unknowingly, had captured her heart. Recalling his mention of 'for some time' when saying she must stay at the castle, Kim began to wonder just how long that was meant to be. Alexandra had left the castle, so the marriage had achieved its objective. There could be a separation without the woman ever learning of it, since Kim could be said to be merely on a prolonged visit to her own country. An annulment or just an agreed separation . . . it mattered little either way so long as she could leave the castle and the man who—now that she loved him—could hurt her abominably with his contempt or his indifference. Yes, she mused, to get away was the wisest move she could make; it would be impossible to go on like this, her love growing stronger, yet with no hope of reciprocation.

Almost without her own volition, her eyes were drawn to the communicating door, and on an impulse quite beyond her control she walked towards it and knocked quietly. A silence followed, as if the occupant were doubting he had heard right. But even as she raised her hand to repeat the knock, the massive oaken door swung away and she looked into her husband's face. She noticed the uplifted brows, the rather haughty stare of enquiry in eyes that marked her pallor, the pose of suspicion, as if he were half inclined to suspect her of bringing him to the door on some trivial pretext.

All these combined to disconcert her but she marshalled enough courage to say, 'Vidas, I know it's late, but I'd like to talk to you.'

'Talk?' The hooded dark eyes travelled over her figure in slow and sensual appraisal, and a moment's reflection convinced Kim that this was certainly not the time to ask him to discuss the possibility of a separation. 'Couldn't it have waited until morning?' He came forward as he spoke; Kim saw the cord of his dressing gown begin to slip, allowing the front edges to fall open. She found it difficult to maintain her composure as she began moving backwards, having no other alternative as he continued to come towards her.

'Yes,' she gulped hastily. 'Tomorrow will do—it—it will do fine!' She was trembling with sudden fear as she tried to halt his approach. But the only way would be to stop altogether . . . and he was far too close already.

'Why did you knock?' He still came on with quiet deliberation and now Kim was by the bed, only a step from it.

All colour left her face, for the look in his eyes was an unmistakable warning of danger. 'To—to tell you something. But as you—you s-say, it will keep until tomorrow.'

Her heart raced as nameless sensations shot through her brain. Allowing her sense of urgency to control her actions, she had been fool enough to knock at his door attired as she was, with every curve, every line and shadow of her body revealed through the transparency of her nightgown! It was a crazy thing to do—especially as she had already sensed his interest, had actually feared, at one time, that he might decide to put their marriage on a normal footing.

'What is it you want to tell me, Kim?' Soft the tone but edged with contempt. She gasped at the conviction that he actually believed she wanted him to make love to her!

'It was nothing,' she began tremulously.

'That will not suffice, my dear. What is this playacting all about? If you want me to sleep with you, then why not say so?'

'Oh—you're hateful—!' She took another strategic step backwards as his hand shot out, but her wrist was locked within his fingers and there was no escape as he jerked her trembling body to him, took her chin in his hand and, forcing her head back, brought his hard demanding mouth down on hers. She felt the moist exploration, was compelled by his insistent strength to part her lips, and a quiver of reluctant pleasure throbbed through her entire frame as his tongue touched hers. She panted as suffocating heat spread through her. Yet, instinctively, she struggled, pushing her clenched fists against his chest. Leaning away, he grasped both of her hands in one of his and pushed them behind her back, and she found herself subjected to the kind of ardent lovemaking that almost immediately awakened her own desires.

She was at the mercy of a lover practised in the art, with the finesse of a man who was confident of swift surrender, and Kim had no resistance when his hand, sliding into the dipped neckline of her frail covering, took and caressed one small firm breast, the experienced fingers coaxing the nipple with slow and calculated mastery. Tremors of sheer ecstasy quivered through her veins as her heart began to beat at an exhilarating rate. She pressed against the whipcord hardness of his frame, obediently arching her body in response to his unspoken command. Small and helpless, she was the victim of his desires and of his determination to conquer. She thrilled to the roving exploration of his hands, and her own came up to encircle his neck, to caress his nape.

But when one lean hand slid along the length of her spine and she felt her nightgown lifted, she uttered a protest and at the same time marshalled unexpected strength to push her hands against his chest. Freeing herself, she staggered away, her heart pounding against her rib cage, every nerve within her stretched almost to the breaking point.

'Go away!' she cried after gulping for air. 'Get out of here this very minute!'

He stood looking at her, calm and unruffled, a smile of mocking amusement on his face. 'I must admit that I'd half expected the approach, but I didn't anticipate the little act you're putting on . . . Not that it is new to me,' he added with a reflective laugh. 'It's a woman's prerogative to assume the reluctant pose; in fact, almost all the females of the species are similarly affected, though heaven knows why, when they're even more eager than the males.' He took a step towards her and she cried out for him to leave her alone.

'Go away, I said!' She turned and ran for the door, knowing all the while that there was no possibility of getting it open in time even if she managed to reach it—which she did not. Her husband's firm grip on her arm brought her round to face him; he took a handful of hair to force her head back, and tears sprang to her eyes at the pain and humiliation of her position. His dark pagan eyes roved over her body, his fingers tracing the curves of her cheeks, her throat, her heaving breasts. And all the while she dared not move because he held her so firmly by the hair. The tears fell, and she noticed his hand become wet. 'I hate you,' she whispered. 'You haven't kept to your side of the bargain we made.'

'*We* made?' with a lift of his straight black brows. 'I never made any bargain with you that I know of.' Again the amorous eyes roved, and she coloured when he seemed fascinated by what he saw. 'You wanted marriage and I consented—'

'I wanted a settlement,' she broke in, then sagged and shook her head. 'What does it matter? Please go away and leave me alone. You said it wasn't to be a normal marriage.'

He was puzzled, she noticed, and her hopes ran high.

'Are you really serious? You want me to leave you?' He released her hair and she automatically put a hand to the back of her head where the pain was. 'If you didn't want me to sleep with you, then what reason did you have for knocking on my door?'

'It was to tell you something.' She moved, sat down on the bed, then jumped up so swiftly that her action brought a laugh from her husband's lips.

'Well,' he said after a long moment of considering, 'whatever the reason for your wanting to see me tonight it was a mistake—if you had no wish for me to stay.'

'What . . . ?'

'Yes, my dear, I intend to stay. I've been tempted, and you have enough experience of men to know that I'm at the point of no return.' He reached out; she began to cry again but made no move to resist him, admitting that what he said was true: he was at the point of no return. Inexperienced as she was, she did possess enough intelligence to read what was in his eyes. Even if he had not been her husband, her chances of escape would have been exceedingly slender . . . and she *was* his wife. . . .

His kisses were like fire on her lips; his exploring hands held both temptation and compulsion; the mastery of his body rendered her helpless and submissive. She wanted him long before he carried her to the bed, for erupting emotions had set every nerve on fire and only complete fulfillment would assuage the agonising yearning within her. He lay down beside her; she

DESIRE

quivered beneath his warm exploring hands, moaning softly, as fierce yearning for the final act consumed every fibre in her body. She was just about to give herself up completely when, with the speed of a comet, the danger light appeared in her brain, and jerking up, she escaped his hands as she leapt from the bed, her chest heaving, her legs like jelly beneath her.

'I can't' she cried, gesturing wildly with her hands. She was terrified of what he would discover and in a frenzy of self-protection, she stumbled across the room, making for the door.

'What the devil's come over you!' Leaping from the bed, Vidas caught her just as she was wrenching the door open. 'Are you mad? Is it your intention to parade before the servants dressed like that?' With a vicious jerk he sent her back across the room, then closed the door and turned the key. Kim stared, eyes dilating, as he came slowly towards her.

'I—I forgot I h-had only my nightdress on,' she choked.

The dark brows lifted fractionally. 'That's a strange thing to forget, isn't it?'

'I won't let you make love to me!' she cried. 'Go away—go back to your room and leave me alone!' Fear put stridency into her voice; she knew she must appear quite mad to him, standing there, ordering him to go after being so close to fulfillment. No wonder he was looking baffled. Should she explain? Risk his fury? The very idea brought a stifling sensation to her throat. 'Go away, I said—' She looked around, then ran to snatch up her robe. 'Leave me alone—I've changed my—my m-mind.'

'Changed your mind, Kim?' So soft the tone, unfathomable the glint in his pagan eyes. 'I'm sorry to tell

84

you, my dear, that you are not allowed to change your mind.' She fought him like a wildcat but to no avail, until, sobbing resignedly, she ceased her struggles. . . .

'So it was all lies. You never slept with my brother . . . or with any other man, for that matter.' Slowly the words came, and so very quietly. Yet Kim, standing fully dressed by the bathroom door, felt herself begin to tremble from head to foot. Would he strangle her? she wondered, almost unable to believe that a man so handsome could look so evil, so dangerously ruthless and without one small degree of mercy.

'Well, have you nothing to say?' Vidas was in the middle of the room, attired in his dressing gown and nothing else. Kim had risen while he was still asleep, and she now wondered why, last night, she had not put up a prolonged fight, knowing as she did that if Vidas made love to her, he was sure to learn of her deceit. But carried away as she had been by the explosive force of his ardour and the intensity of her own reawakened desires, her mind had become closed to all else but the pleasure of the moment. The showdown had seemed a million years away.

But now . . . this was to be the reckoning, and as fear mounted she retreated across the floor, a move that made his eyes grow dark. Yet his voice betrayed nothing beyond a soft command as he said, pointing to a spot in front of him, 'Come here, Kim.'

She shook her head, automatically pressing a hand to her heart. 'You—you frighten m-me.' She faltered. 'Please go away and—and leave me alone.'

'I said come here.'

Kim's face was deathly white, her legs weak, her body chilled to the bone. She took another faltering step backwards, and it was when her hand touched the door that an incredible transformation took place within her. Why should he have this ability to terrify her? He was a man, not some all-powerful god before whom all other beings had to prostrate themselves! An almost physical surge of fury rose within her, tightening her nerves to give her strength, blinding her to all danger as she said, eyes blazing and fists tight against her sides, 'Don't stand there giving me orders! The marriage suited you as much as it suited me, so what's your complaint?'

His eyes grew darker still. Kim's mouth went dry as he began to move threateningly towards her, but she stood her ground, making no attempt to sidestep him.

'My complaint's the deceit—' His hand shot out, and Kim felt the breath knocked out of her body as she came up against the hardness of his frame, and as she looked up into the smouldering fury of his eyes her courage deserted her and she heard herself whimper, begging for mercy. 'Deceit,' he snarled, cutting her short. 'I sensed you had a secret, knew you were laughing at me and yet I would never have guessed in a million years it was this! '

'I wasn't laughing, Vidas, believe me—' Her pleading words were choked off by the bruising pressure of his mouth. With merciless deliberation he punished her, hurting her body, fastening her arms to her sides, and when he had finished he pushed her from him, an expression of darkest evil on his face. She staggered backwards, found herself sitting on the bed, every nerve cell in her body rioting. She put a hand against her breast, pressing it hard in an attempt to slow the wild throbbing. Weak and drained from the onslaught, she looked up into his pagan face and said feebly, 'Go away—please l-leave me alone. . . .'

He stood for a moment, his lips drawn back, showing his teeth. Kim, choking with renewed fear, lifted a hand, gesturing him to go away.

'We'll talk more about it later,' he said harshly at last, and turning, he went through the communicating door, slamming it closed behind him.

Surprising though it was to Kim, Vidas did not approach her again that day; she did not even see him until just before dinner when he came to her on the verandah, where she was sitting with an open book on her lap.

'We shall keep up appearances before the servants,' he told her brusquely.

'Of course.'

'Everything will go on as before.'

'Yes, Vidas.' She watched him stride away along the length of the verandah and enter the castle through a French window. Everything must go on as before. . . . Kim did not ask herself how long she could stand the strain. She would accept each day as it came and let the next one take care of itself.

Chapter Six

The strained relationship continued for another week, with words passing between them only at dinnertime, and this was purely for appearances sake, to prevent gossip in the kitchen, Vidas said.

Kim was puzzled by his attitude, for although he sometimes appeared to be still smouldering with anger beneath the surface, there were other times when his quiet, withdrawn manner made her feel he was brooding, that the only thing troubling him was injured pride. She had tricked him, deliberately, and his ego had suffered. He believed she had been laughing at him, seeing him as a gullible fool, easily taken in.

And one day, impatient with the way he was going on, she decided to broach the subject herself with a view to making some attempt to explain. Prudently choosing dinnertime for her purpose—for then she would be sure of his not subjecting her to a show of temper—she spoke as soon as they sat down, reminding him that he had said they would talk about the matter later.

'But you haven't mentioned it,' she ended, taking up her napkin and shaking it out over her lap. She saw the sudden glint in his eyes and waited for him to speak.

'Is there anything to talk about?' he asked curtly.

'Yes, a good deal,' she answered, pale but composed. 'You've assumed things that are wrong and you're harbouring hatred against me because of it.' He gave a slight start, which set Kim wondering if the word 'hatred' had struck him as too strong. Dislike, perhaps . . . yes, most certainly dislike!

'Well?' he invited tersely.

'You said I was laughing at you and that wasn't true.'

His teeth snapped together. 'I warned you what to expect if you had a secret and were laughing at me. Aren't you afraid now of what I might do to you?'

'I'm willing to take the risk,' was her quiet rejoinder, 'because I feel that neither of us can go on like this indefinitely.'

Although there was no relaxing of the taut features, Kim did have the impression that he agreed with what she had just said and, as a result, was ready to listen to whatever else she had to say.

'You said your complaint was my deceit,' she began. 'Well, obviously I can't deny deceiving you. But I do deny laughing at you. As for the secret—well, surely you must know it was a burden to me?'

He frowned at her across the table and said, 'Why, in the very beginning, didn't you deny what Dendras had told me?'

'It was owing to your arrogance, and to the fact of your immediately branding me a no-good. I wanted the satisfaction of knowing you'd be worried. But I can tell you now that I had no intention of ever marrying Dendras. He was a mere boy and all he felt for me was calf love and I told him so. I had already given him up before you and I met.'

'Already given him up?' with a look of puzzlement. 'Then why did you and I ever come to meet at all?'

She bit her lip, frowning at the memory of how she had weakened in her resolve not to see Dendras again. 'He was so upset, on the point of tears, and so I agreed to dine with him that Saturday. And that just happened to be the occasion of your visit to him.'

'Is all this the truth?'

'I have nothing to gain by lying at this stage.'

'If you had no intention of marrying Dendras, why didn't you tell me so?'

'I've just told you, because of your attitude towards me. You've yourself to blame for most of it. When you said you'd had information from Dendras, and I asked you what it was, you didn't say!'

'You should have insisted on knowing!'

'Vidas,' she returned quietly, 'you can't blame me for it all. True, believing I was expecting Dendras's child, you quite naturally thought I knew what you were talking about. But you now have to remember that I had no idea at that time that Dendras had told you a lie, or what he *had* told you. Evidently he believed he could persuade me to marry him once he had obtained your consent.'

'And what the devil was he going to tell you afterwards?'

Kim drew an impatient breath. 'Does it matter? For one thing Dendras is dead, and for another even if he hadn't been killed, I had no intention of marrying him!'

'All right, all right,' he said impatiently, 'I'm as muddled as you are over this whole business, but all I know is that you deliberately allowed me to believe you'd slept with my brother!' Anger was now in his voice, and Kim had the odd impression that his wrath stemmed more from the fact that she had allowed him to believe she was a no-good than from the actual deceit itself.

'You accused me of being a gold digger,' she reminded him. 'At one time I was actually on the point of telling you I'd not the slightest intention of marrying Dendras, when you interrupted me and arrogantly told me to *forget* about marrying your brother. I was naturally fuming, bitterly resenting your attitude; it infuriated me. But later I did try again. This time you asked me if I had anything to say in my own defence. Well, what would your reaction be to a thing like that, especially if you knew you were entirely innocent?'

'I expect I'd have reacted in a similar way,' he admitted, and the answer did not really surprise her, for his expression had gradually been changing as she spoke.

'At that time I just could not have said the words that would have given you satisfaction. I wanted to get my own back and the only way was to keep you on tenterhooks.'

'Typically female, and English,' he submitted, and within the jeering irony of his tone, Kim detected a trace of amusement as well.

'Afterwards, when you came to tell me that Dendras was dead, I again thought about telling you the truth, but by then it no longer seemed important because I didn't expect ever to see you again.'

Vidas looked at her with cool deliberation; it was an

unpredictable moment, and in the electric silence, Kim's nerves quivered. Had his fury abated, or did it still smoulder beneath the surface? She tilted her chin; it was a defensive gesture, designed to warn him to be prepared for firmness on her part. For the more she viewed the situation, the less excuse she could find for his putting so much blame on her. And in any case, as she had earlier pointed out, the marriage was as beneficial to him as it was to her. At last he spoke, in a quiet voice, to ask the reason why she had knocked on his bedroom door that night.

'It obviously wasn't for the reason I assumed,' he added with amused mockery. 'The very last thing you'd have wanted was for your deceit to be discovered.'

'I wanted to discuss the possibility of a separation,' she told him. 'It could be arranged so that Alexandra will not know about it.'

'There'll be no separation.' His tone was almost harsh with finality. 'You're my wife and it stays that way; I thought I'd already made that clear.'

'You said it would only be for a time.'

'I also said that my stepmother might take it into her head to return if she knew we had separated.'

'But she needn't know. I've just said so. I could merely be on a trip to England, then stay there—'

'Put the idea out of your head,' he advised, almost glowering at her across the dinner table. 'Dare to leave me and I shall immediately get in touch with your mother to inform her of everything that has happened.'

'Are you blackmailing me?' she asked.

'Be very careful,' he recommended, dark eyes glinting.

'I don't believe you would be so cruel to my parents,'

said Kim, reflecting on that profound moment when her mother and Vidas had stared into one another's eyes. 'You're just saying that as a threat.'

'Don't try me, Kim,' he said. 'I'm very satisfied with our marriage and have no desire to end it.'

'So I must stay with you . . . for always?' To remain forever with a man who neither loved nor respected her would be an impossibility, she decided. 'I'll work to repay what you have spent on my parents, Vidas,' she said, and at the plea in her voice he seemed to frown. 'To stay together, living as man and wife, without love—' She shook her head vehemently. 'It would be immoral,' she said finally, and colour flooded her cheeks when he threw back his head and laughed.

'Greeks care nothing either for love or for immorality,' he assured her. 'The demands of the flesh are all that we care about.'

Kim shot him a glance, her senses alerted by something in his tone. She felt he was adopting a pose, the reason for which was obscure. There was a shuttered expression in his eyes, and she had the extraordinary conviction that he was out of his accustomed element, that he was temporarily lacking in that arrogant self-assurance which carried him so confidently through every situation. The impression was fleeting but unmistakable, and Kim knew she would think about it over and over again, always with puzzlement and the conviction that if only she could have seen into his mind at that moment, she would have learnt something of immense value. But alas, it was impossible to read the thoughts of a man like Vidas.

Two days later she telephoned her parents. They had written to tell her what time they would be at their friends' apartment, and as soon as she heard her mother's happy tone, Kim's heart lightened. Whatever might come to her in the future, whatever the heart-aches, she would never regret what she had done.

'It's so wonderful here, Kim, darling! The lovely sunshine, the freedom from worry, the kindness of our friends—oh, I don't know why we should be so lucky. It's all due to you, of course, dear Kim, and we love you dearly for finding that charming Vidas and marrying him!'

'I'm so glad everything is all right. I take it that Father's condition is continuing to improve?'

'Yes, love—and here he is, impatient to talk to you.'

'Hello, Kim! Yes, I'm improving all the time. I even took a swim in the pool this morning, and this after-noon we're going along to the shops to stock up for the weekend.'

'You sound as if you're having fun.'

'We are! We both feel young again!'

'You *are* young,' said Kim on a note of mock severity. 'Just you remember that. Age is merely an attitude of mind, and once you begin to think you're getting old, then the rot really sets in.'

'I'll remember.' He laughed. Oh, but it was good to hear a sound like that coming over the line! Yes, it had all been worth it, decided Kim again. 'We made a pact never to think of Stephen or to speak of him. It might be selfish, Kim, but we feel we did all we could for him, and to worry about him now would be fruitless.'

'And would impair your health again. You are not selfish, Father—neither of you could ever be that. So enjoy yourselves. You're all right for money?'

'Fine! We don't live luxuriously, but we're very

comfortable and well fed.' Another laugh before he went on. 'We've bought nice new furniture and the flat was decorated before we moved in. So everything is new and gleaming. . . . You and Vidas ought to come over for a visit,' he added, as the thought occurred to him. 'How about it?'

'I'll speak to him' she promised, not allowing her speculations to go any further than that, even though there had been a dramatic improvement in their relationship since she had cleared the air.

'You sound so happy. How is it, living on a lovely Greek island?'

'Wonderful. Malindos is a small island and not too touristy yet. Some of the cruise ships stop, and we have a few very charming hotels.'

'And you live in a castle.' A small silence followed before he said, 'You haven't sent any photographs yet, love, and we know nothing of the place.'

'I've taken some snapshots and I'll finish the roll quite soon, then I'll send you the best ones.'

'Plenty of you with Vidas, remember.'

'All right.'

Kim spoke to her mother again, and when eventually she put the receiver back on its rest, she realised that Vidas was standing behind her.

'You heard?' She gave a small sigh and added, 'They believe I'm deliriously happy.'

The look he gave her was unfathomable. 'Aren't you happy?'

She lifted her eyes to his, puzzled by his expression. Could it be possible that Vidas was wishing that she and he could have met in different circumstances? A wild hope for the future was born, and try as she would to dismiss it, she found it impossible to do so. And suddenly her heart was light and the tender smile fluttered to lips that had quivered only seconds ago.

'Perhaps, one day, I shall be happy,' she said, and her husband's expression instantly became closed.

'I gather that your father wanted some snapshots of you and me together,' he said, bypassing her comment.

'Yes; he asked for plenty.' She looked hopefully at him and he nodded his head.

'We'll get Andreas to take some. He's rather good with a camera.'

Andreas was the manservant whose role was mainly that of butler, but he was a general handyman about the castle and Vidas had once said that he was almost indispensable.

'When can he take them?' she wanted to know. 'I'd like to get them off as soon as possible.'

'This afternoon, if that is what you'd like.'

'That will be fine. Thank you, Vidas.'

His dark eyes held a mysterious light as they looked down into her face. 'For what?' he asked quietly.

'For agreeing to have the snaps taken.'

'We must keep your parents happy,' was all he said to that.

It was much later, when they were having dinner in the gracious salon, that Kim mentioned the visit to Spain. But she immediately added, 'I didn't promise anything because I knew you'd not want to go.'

His dark eyes flickered, taking in her fluctuating colour, the deep beauty of her eyes, the tremulous movement of her lips. She saw a muscle working in his throat and was profoundly affected by the silence and the presence of the man she loved.

'What makes you so sure I'd not want to go?'

enquired Vidas at last, and Kim instantly registered surprise . . . and pleasure too, for her heart was light again, just as it had been earlier.

'Well, I naturally felt you'd not want to go on a holiday with me.'

'Perhaps we shall consider it,' he returned, watching the effect of candleglow on her hair, bringing out lights and colours even Kim did not know were there. 'Not for a while, though, because I have things to do. I must go to the capital in two weeks time, and I'll be away for about four or five days.'

'On business?' A weight settled on her stomach at the thought of his being away from the castle. 'I . . . er . . . couldn't go with you?' Hope was in her glance and in her heart. 'I'd not make a nuisance of myself.'

He shook his head, yet she had the strange impression that he was forcing himself to utter words he would rather not have spoken. 'No, I can't take you with me. I have too much to do and you'd be on your own all the time.' He paused a moment, examining her face, watching for any change of expression. 'You seem to be forgetting that ours is not a normal marriage.'

'I haven't forgotten,' she denied in gentle tones, 'but, just now, you said we might go to Spain together, and so—so I had the courage to ask if I could accompany you to Athens.' She was embarrassed, awkward, unsure of herself in spite of the mention just now of courage. He was far too overpowering, this dark Greek who was her husband, too aware of his own superiority.

'Another time, perhaps,' was all he said, and his voice had taken on an edge of harshness, as if he were regretting his kindness to her in agreeing to the snapshots and in making the half-promise to go to Spain with her. What an enigma he was!

97

When dinner was over he surprised her by suggesting a walk in the grounds. 'I've been busy in my study for most of the day,' he added by way of explanation, 'and I feel the need of some fresh air.'

Happy that he should want her company, Kim jumped up at once, ready to go out immediately.

'You'll need some kind of a wrap,' he said.

'Oh, no—'

'Go and fetch one,' he broke in authoritatively. 'I'll be waiting in the hall.'

'It's really quite warm, Vidas,' she began to protest, when a flick of his hand stopped her.

'Kim,' he said in a very soft voice, 'do as I say.'

She coloured, blinked at him, then went off to do his bidding. Was he really anxious about her feeling cold, or merely exerting his authority, demonstrating his mastery over her? There was no answer, and in any case it was of no importance, because either way, his order had made her happy.

They went out into the starlight and shadows, the air around them pulsing with the noise of cicadas in the olive trees on the hillside and the perfume of exotic flowers drifting on the breeze.

'It's beautiful out here.' Kim breathed, warmth in her heart that had nothing at all to do with the air temperature. The whole garden was lit up by the full moon sailing in the purple sky and the lamps hidden in the trees. The star-spangled sky was a radiant canopy above the silver-tinted sea and white-sanded shore, fringed by palms and carob trees. Kim and Vidas wandered slowly along the various paths separating the flower beds and smooth velvet lawns, their eyes repeatedly wandering down to the glory and serenity of the shoreline and the sparkling water beyond. On the horizon a ship's presence was betrayed by its lights, and closer to the shore several *caïques* bobbed about, lanterns swaying, while their owners sought for the catch that would earn them the money they needed for their meagre existence. A poor island, mainly, yet there was happiness and contentment among the inhabitants.

'You like Greece, then?'

'What I've seen of it. I believe there are hundreds of islands, some uninhabited.'

'That's right. We have many beautiful islands that *are* inhabited, some that are only sparsely inhabited, while others—mainly those where tourism has thrived—are somewhat overcrowded.' He talked on for a while, with Kim content to listen, though feeling at a certain loss in spite of the pleasure she derived from her husband's company. She desperately wanted physical contact, the touch of his hand, the caress of his lips.

Almost as if sensing her desires, Vidas stopped and turned to her, his eyes darker than ever as they looked down into her face. 'You're very beautiful,' he murmured, his hand touching her brow, sweeping back tendrils of hair that had been sent awry by a puff of wind gently cascading from the foothills of the mountains. These latter were stark in the moonlight, tortured lava heights, naked and untamed by man. 'I know so little about you,' Vidas said, his hand still gentle on her brow. Kim swayed close, vitally aware of his magnetism, of the incredible height and impression of power, of the heady scent of after-shave—or was it body lotion? It reminded her of the fresh tang of the sea, or of a breeze carrying the scent of heather across a wide expanse of moorland. 'Tell me something about your life in England.'

'It wasn't very interesting,' she returned, not wanting

to talk, but merely to have him hold her close, so that she could feel the strength of his masculinity, the hardness of his frame against the yielding softness of her own. 'After Father's first heart attack we rarely went anywhere. And we were relatively poor. . . .' Her voice trailed away to silence. 'You can't possibly be interested,' she asserted after a pause.

'You had no brothers or sisters?'

'No, just Stephen, whom my parents adopted.'

'You haven't heard anything about him?'

Kim shook her head. Vidas had removed his hand; she missed its smooth warmth and gentleness, but somehow she could still feel some slight sensation of its presence. 'We're no longer interested in what is happening to him,' she admitted. 'It may seem heartless to you, but he has caused us so much trouble already.'

'I don't consider it heartless. We each have a life of our own; it's our most precious possession, and if we waste it on people who are underserving, then we are exceedingly foolish. Life is too short to waste, Kim.' So serious the tone, so sincere the words he uttered. Kim's love swelled within her and she lifted her face, lips quivering and slightly parted, inviting his kiss. For a long moment he seemed to be fighting an inner battle, while breathless, she waited, her heart throbbing with hope even while she knew a certain fear that he would ignore her invitation. She was fighting for his love; she smiled and his expression changed. Her nerves caught as his head came down, and then she was thrilling to the touch of his lips, the strength of his encircling arms, the masterful pressure of his body as it melded with hers so that she was vitally aware of his masculinity, of the vibrant intensity of his desire for her.

'I love you,' she whispered silently, and with tender abandon she moved her body in joyful rhythm with his.

'My heavens, but you're different!' His mouth was cruel suddenly and sensually exploring; his hands possessed her with the arrogant mastery that had already thrilled her, that set him far above her, making her his suppliant, the willing victim of his pagan instincts. She was crushed to his hard body and looked up to see dark eyes smouldering with passion about to burst into flame. They settled on her breasts, then moved to the delectable curve of her throat. Wild emotion spread through every nerve cell in her body, invading any centre of resistance she might have had; her limbs went weak even while her desire gained momentum, quickening her responses so that her hand slid inside his shirt and around him, her fired senses thrilling to the contact with his bare flesh.

'Come,' he exclaimed hoarsely, and lightly swung her off her feet. 'It's late . . . far too late to be out here!'

Chapter Seven

Although she enjoyed the tranquil hours she spent in the lovely grounds of the castle, Kim was restless, and of course the simple explanation was that her husband was away from home. He had phoned to say his stay in Athens would have to be extended but had not felt the necessity of adding an explanation. It was a business visit she knew, and before he left he had warned her that it might have to be prolonged.

Kim's uneasy mind insisted on reminding her of the possibility that, despite her resolve to try to win her husband's love, Vidas might forever remain as remote as he was at present. On going away he had thought fit to remind her that theirs was not a normal marriage, and he was not, of course, referring to the physical side, which was now perfectly normal, fulfilling their desires in a way that could not be faulted. Compatibility was supreme; no couple wildly in love could have given each other more than they did. For Kim, detachment from reality was complete; it was as if she became a disembodied spirit floating in a realm of languid emotion and idealistic dreams, where love was, and she knew the ecstasy of giving and receiving in all its primordial purity and willing sacrifice. And, passionate though her husband was, his way with her was now characterised by respect and gentleness and the firm resolve that she should never be disappointed. And so her love for him had flourished and increased until, at those intimate times, it overflowed, and she was amazed that he had not discovered the secret of her heart. Sometimes she wished he would discover it, so that she could see what his reaction would be; at other times she squirmed at the idea, sure her humiliation would be such as to cause a rift, or at least a coolness in her attitude towards his lovemaking. And if this should happen, Vidas might have second thoughts and decide he wanted his freedom, especially as there was no longer any possibility of Alexandra returning to the castle. She had recently sent word that she wanted several items that she claimed were hers; she had moved to the island of Rhodes, and as she had taken a large house, she would require some furniture and other necessities from her former home. Vidas had made no objection and the servants had been busy collecting these items together, ready to be delivered when Alexandra gave the word.

Realising how much her thoughts had wandered, Kim returned to her earlier musings. No, Vidas had not been referring to the physical side of their marriage; he was reminding her that it had not been based on love. Yet there were times when in some inexplicable way she had sensed more in his lovemaking than the mere assuaging of a physical need. She could not put her finger on it but felt it to be there. Could it be possible that, once he had been disillusioned about his first estimation of her character, he was now finding himself drawn to her in an entirely different way from the purely physical? But if so, why the restraint he put upon his feelings for her? The only feasible answer was that, determined as he had always been not to become emotionally involved with a woman, he was making a supreme effort to hold on to his original intention. A faint smile hovered on Kim's lips as she continued to ponder this in the light of her own anxious uncertainty. Her recent all-embracing pessimism became vague, then vanished altogether as she found herself refusing to accept that he was beyond her reach.

One morning, a few days after Vidas's departure for the capital, Kim felt so restless that she decided to take a long walk, exploring a wider circle of her surroundings, and she found herself heading for the castle on the cliff where the Greek lived with his Irish wife. Although not expecting to see the girl, Kim hoped she would, and just as she reached the imposing wrought-iron gates a young woman emerged, swinging a large sun hat in her hand.

Without a moment's hesitation Kim said brightly, 'Good afternoon. It's a lovely day.'

The girl stopped and blinked, then a smile spread over her face. In the few seconds before she responded to her greeting, Kim examined the girl's face. She saw the typical Irish colleen look—fine bone structure and thin features, clear peach-tinted skin and rosy lips. Her hair was dark, contrasting with the vivid blue of her eyes.

'Hello! So you are the bride of Vidas Christou! I'd

hoped we'd meet soon. Please come into my home and have some refreshment.'

'I'd love to,' agreed Kim happily. 'I must admit that I too had hoped we'd meet. It's nice to hear one's own language spoken without an accent.'

'But I do have an accent.' The girl laughed and then told Kim to call her Bridie.

'My name's Kim,' was the immediate response as she fell into step with the girl, who had turned back into the long, tree-shaded drive.

'My husband's name is Georgios; naturally I call him George.' Bridie was swinging along, her dark hair flowing; she was happy and it showed in every vital movement, in every turn of her head that revealed her animated countenance. Kim sighed, envying her, yet somehow this meeting with the girl set her own hopes for happiness soaring. She felt lighter in heart, even more optimistic about making her husband fall in love with her. 'Here we are. My husband's not in at present, but you must come again—or perhaps we might call on you?'

'Anytime.' Kim smiled, feeling she had already made a friend. 'Do you have a lot of free time? I mean, have you any children?'

'Not yet. We keep trying,' Bridie added with a sudden grimace, 'but no luck! However, we've not been married quite two years yet, and so we remain optimistic.'

The castle was similar in construction to the Castello Astura, which was not surprising since they were both built by the Venetians. Bridie clapped her hands to bring a servant, and Kim had to smile at this habit she had obviously acquired from her husband. It was quite customary for a Greek man to summon his employees in this way. The girl who came in response was small and slender with dusky skin, raven hair, and a wide smile which highlighted several gold fillings. Her husband worked as head gardener on the estate. Bridie ordered tea and cakes and suggested they have these refreshments on the back patio, which at this time of day was flooded with sunshine. The sea lay still and blue before them, the sky a sapphire canopy, cloudless and brittle.

'You have a magnificent view,' commented Kim, helping herself to a delicious pastry filled with fresh cream and topped with nuts.

'Your view is just as spectacular, but in a different way.'

'Yes. You've been to the Castello Astura, obviously?'

'When Dendras was there he sometimes threw a party, and everyone was invited. It was dreadfully sad about him,' reflected Bridie, suddenly grave. 'And now his mother's gone, we hear?'

'That's right.'

'It was laid down in old Mr. Christou's will that she must leave on Vidas's marriage.' Kim said nothing, and after a moment Bridie said, a curious ring to her soft Irish brogue, 'How did you get along with her? Or is that too personal a question for you to answer?'

Kim had to smile at the girl's open curiosity. She was willing to risk a rebuff in order to satisfy that curiosity. 'I didn't get on with her very well,' she confessed. 'But even her own son seemed to have differences with her.'

'Everyone did. But it was rumored that your husband especially could not abide her and about a year ago he almost—' Bridie stopped short, colouring up as she put a hand to her mouth.

Kim could not help saying, noticing the girl's avoidance of her stare, 'Almost . . . what, Bridie?'

The other girl shrugged her shoulders. 'It was nothing.' She took up a small wedge of pastry she had cut from the larger piece on her plate and raised it to her mouth. 'Forget it, please.'

But Kim found it impossible to do so. She wanted to know more, perhaps because of her paucity of knowledge about her husband's past life. 'I satisfied your curiosity just now,' she reminded Bridie gently, 'so I expect you to satisfy mine.'

'It's so personal,' began Bridie, a trifle distressed. 'Er . . . can I pour you another cup of tea?'

Kim frowned, biting her lip. She said she would have her cup refilled. 'The Christou family have lived at the castle for a long time, haven't they?'

'It's always been in the family. Well, for several generations,' answered Bridie, pouring the tea. 'It's a beautiful place. I love the sunken pools in the terrace and the serene nobility of the setting. Although ours is on the cliff, I have always thought that yours has the finer setting.'

Kim said nothing. Bridie had spoken without raising her lids, and Kim knew she was talking for talking's sake, just so that Kim would not have the chance to reintroduce the subject of Vidas, and what he had almost done a year ago. 'What part of Ireland do you come from?' enquired Kim conversationally when at last Bridie fell silent.

'The west—Galway.'

'I believe it's beautiful.'

'I think so,' she returned with pride. 'I never expected to leave it—not ever.'

'How did you meet George?' asked Kim interestedly, and was told that Bridie had been working in an hotel when Georgios came to stay as a guest on holiday.

'It was love at first sight.' Bridie laughed reflectively. 'It often is with Greeks.'

'But not many Greeks fall in love at all.'

'You mean they've a reputation for being amorous and unfaithful?' Bridie was amused but nodded all the same. 'It's true, unfortunately for many wives. However, Greek girls don't often expect love, so they don't attach too much importance to it. The status of wife and mother is usually what they're aiming at from an early age.' A pause followed this before Bridie added, eyeing her newfound friend curiously, 'How did you and Vidas come to meet?'

Kim had anticipated the question and merely answered that she had met Vidas through his brother.

'Dendras?' with a fractional lift of her brows. 'How come?'

It was a difficult topic, one which Kim, understandably, meant to avoid embarking on, so she gave a laugh and said lightly, 'You expect me to satisfy your curiosity when you refuse to satisfy mine?'

'It isn't quite the same,' protested Bridie.

'The fact remains that you whetted my appetite for knowledge, then withheld it.'

'Oh, all right,' returned Bridie with a shrug of resignation. 'About a year ago Vidas began paying a good deal of attention to a distant cousin of George's who visits us frequently, and everyone believed he was on the point of asking her to marry him, just so he could get his stepmother out of the house.'

'On the point . . .' Kim murmured, recalling Vidas's comments regarding his attitude towards marriage. It would appear he had been driven almost to the very end of his patience. 'And now,' she said as the idea occurred to her, 'does everyone believe this to be the reason for his marrying me?' The question came out swiftly, before Kim could check it.

'No, of course not!'

'You needn't spare my feelings, Bridie. It would be natural for people to reach the same conclusion now as they did then.' Kim was perfectly calm; it was Bridie who was uncomfortable.

'Vidas was bound to fall in love one day,' she managed after a slight pause. 'I for one do not think he married you for the specific purpose of ridding himself of that horrid woman.' Another pause and then, 'You're so pretty that he would be bound to fall in love with you.'

Kim coloured but soon regained her composure. She said nothing and the subject changed as Bridie asked Kim how she was passing her time on an island where there was little to do beyond what nature itself could provide. Kim owned that she was rather lost now that her husband was away, but said she enjoyed the house and grounds, and exploring the countryside. And at last she rose to go, promising to come again but extending an invitation to Bridie to come over to see her.

'I'll phone you first,' promised Bridie, as she went with Kim to the gate. 'It'll not be this week because I have some charity work to do.'

They said good-bye and Kim walked home slowly, the thought uppermost in her mind that Vidas had, only a year before, been driven almost to marriage. But he had obviously thought better of it, a circumstance that did not in the least surprise Kim, because she could not for one moment imagine Vidas acting impulsively, doing something he knew he might eventually regret. His marriage to her was different, a decision which had been coloured by a purpose other than that of ridding himself of his stepmother. Vidas had believed that an heir was to be born. Yes, his marriage to Kim had been a calculated move, which he had thought he would never regret. Already the marriage in name only had become much more than he intended, and although he had no love for her, he was happy with a relationship which, for her, fulfilled the desires of the mind and body if not the heart. She found divine enchantment in their intimacy; it had a rare beauty, which, if he should ever come to love her, would take them as close to paradise as it was possible to be. Dreams . . . ? Perhaps, but not pipe dreams, not with the vow she had made herself.

Chapter Eight

It was a cordial, intimate evening which followed Vidas's homecoming in the early afternoon. Kim was in the garden when the car, taken to the harbour by Akis, one of the manservants, bowled along the wide avenue of trees and slid to a halt on the forecourt of the castle. Vidas had phoned earlier to give Kim the approximate time of arrival of the *Knossos*, the ferry boat from the port of Piraeus, and she felt excited ever since.

She made sure she would be close by when the car arrived, and as she came forward Vidas was easing his long athletic body from the backseat. She waited for his response to the quivering smile of welcome that hovered on her lips, but he frowned instead, his dark eyes scanning her body from head to toe. It was a tense, electrified moment, characterised by desire on Kim's part, the exquisitely exciting yearning of a woman for her dearly loved husband, but on his part . . . what? His eyes had fixed themselves on the delectable curves above her slender waist, and she sensed the primitive desire of passion, for physical contact with her body. If only he would take her in his arms and kiss her, tell her he had missed her!

'Did you have a profitable trip?' she asked, compelled to break the silence.

'As usual, yes,' he said casually, as his eyes wandered momentarily to the stocky figure of Akis, who was taking the suitcases from the boot of the car. 'And how have you gone on?' He stepped a little closer to her before turning towards the massive oaken door of the castle.

'I've occupied myself all right,' she answered, wishing she could have said just how eagerly she had awaited his return.

He left her in the hall, and to her disappointment, she did not see him again until she almost bumped into him several hours later as he came from his study. She was going up to change for dinner and later, as the communicating door was ajar, she heard him moving about in his bedroom. Just as she was about to go down, the door opened and he stood there, tall, distinguished, impeccably attired in a superbly cut suit of buff-coloured linen, the gleaming whiteness of his shirt a startling contrast to the Arab darkness of his skin. She looked at his hair, gleaming and dark, sprinkled with silver at the temples. She caught her breath, suddenly awed by the sheer magnificence of him; he was like a Greek god, arrogantly aware of his superiority and his power. But as they stood there staring at one another it was as if, almost against his will, he could no longer remain impervious to her charms, and a slow smile dawned, spreading warmth to her veins and happiness to her heart. His hand beckoned and she went to him, obedient to the silent command.

'You're beautiful!' He caught her to him, locking his lips to hers. She clung to him, a diversity of emotions assailing her. On the one hand she was fully aware of the danger that he would guess at her feelings for him, but at the same time she was quite unable to control her eagerness to be in his arms. Her small hands slid round his neck, her caressing fingers feather-light in their tender movement from his throat to his nape. She felt a quiver shoot through him and leant back, eager to note his expression. The gleam of passion shone in his eyes, but there was a whimsical quality about the sensual mouth, which made Kim suspect he was deriving amusement from her curiosity. Swift and delicate colour swept her cheeks; her lashes fluttered down as she attempted to hide her expression from his all-seeing gaze. She felt his fingers beneath her chin, forcing it up as he compelled her to look at him. He stared into her lovely eyes for a long moment before bending his head to take her lips in a prolonged and sensual kiss that took her to the dizzy heights of ecstasy. She closed her eyes, abandoning herself to the rapture of the moment, vitally conscious of the tantalising smell of expensive after-shave lotion, which mingled with the more pungent smell of newly laundered linen.

His mouth against her cheek was moist as he asked, 'What are you thinking, my beautiful wife?'

'I'm just happy,' she answered lightly. And, after a fractional hesitation, 'Are you happy, Vidas?'

'Of course. How could it be otherwise when I own such a beautiful woman, own her body and soul?'

Kim knew she should have resented the conceit in his

tone, and the unmistakable hint of mockery, but her desires were too intense for her to take exception to anything her husband did or said. She had missed him unbearably and now he was home; the relief was joy, happiness, emotional contentment. Her winning smile challenged him, and to her satisfaction, his face softened. When he kissed her it was with gentleness not unmingled with tender passion, and his hands were warm and caressing when presently they came round to frame her face. A suffusion of delicate colour rose in her cheeks as he continued to gaze down into her eyes, and a swift, involuntary laugh escaped him as he said, 'You're very young, my dear.'

'You once said I was almost thirty,' she could not help reminding him, a twinkle of amusement replacing the dreamy expression in her eyes.

'Never!' he denied. 'How could I?'

She felt obliged to explain, because he was looking attentively at her, awaiting her reply.

'Oh, then.' He tossed the matter off with a nonchalant gesture of his hand. 'Things were very different.' His fingers began tracing a line from one high cheekbone to her throat. 'You turned out to be very different from what I had been given to understand.'

'So you're not sorry you married me?'

The dark eyes glimmered with an unfathomable light. 'What are you asking me, Kim?'

'It was a simple question.'

'With hidden meaning.'

Did he guess that she was willing him to say he loved her? 'You're imagining things.' Confusion was difficult to conceal, and she buried her face in his shoulder, aware of the muscled hardness of his chest and the even beating of his heart.

It seemed that a sigh escaped him before, holding her at arms length, he said, 'Come, it's time we were going down.'

Adela, one of the housemaids, had gone to rather more trouble with the table than usual. There were deep red roses at one end and small individual flower arrangements beside the plates. Candles flickered in their antique silver holders, while crystal and gleaming cutlery scintillated in the golden candleglow, which, subtly blending with the amber reflection from the wall lights, bathed the entire room in an atmosphere of mellowed elegance reminiscent of a bygone age.

With his customary fastidious attention to etiquette, Vidas pulled out his wife's chair for her and saw her seated; she felt the thrill of his lips on her hair and was glad she had used an exotic, perfumed shampoo earlier in the day.

'Tell me what you've been doing with yourself,' invited Vidas, as he sat down facing her.

She told him about her meeting with Bridie and went on to say she had invited her to come over sometime. 'You don't mind?' she ended a trifle uneasily.

He shook his head. 'Not at all. I have never been overfriendly with the Grivases, but I met them several times when Dendras gave his parties.'

'Shall we invite them to dinner sometime?' she asked animatedly.

Her husband's eyes flickered. 'You're anxious to make a friend from your own part of the world, it would seem.'

'Yes. It was nice to talk to Bridie.' A small pause and then, 'She seems very happy.'

'It was love at first sight. She probably told you?' His tone held a hint of mocking satire.

'It *is* possible for people to fall in love on sight, Vidas, even though you sneer at the idea.'

He said nothing more about it and a friendly silence reigned until, as they were eating the dessert, he said they would take a stroll in the garden when the meal was over.

There had been a swift flurry of rain while they were having dinner, and when they went out, it was into a nebulous curtain of darkness which made Kim instantly seek her husband's hand. But they had not been walking for more than five minutes when the clear silver sphere of the moon emerged from behind the fast-disintegrating clouds. The gardens were suddenly bathed with moonlight, and the rejoicing splendour of earth and sky after the rain was something that could be felt with more then the senses; it was a physical awareness of all that was totally unsullied—pure and fresh and clean. Glancing up at her husband's profile, Kim caught her breath, wondering how she had come to be married to such a man. And naturally her thoughts sped on to the possibility of his one day falling in love with her. It would be a miracle . . . but miracles sometimes happened.

She and Vidas walked on, hands still clasped even though the moon was flooding the landscape with light. Kim tried to speak, to break the silence, then suddenly had no wish to break it, for there had come over her a vague yet all-embracing sense of isolation, as if she were quite alone in the stillness of the castle grounds, cut off from the world . . . She stared unseeingly into space, and in her heart and mind reigned a peace that was absolute.

Then, plaintively into the silence, came the distant cry of a donkey, tethered on a lonely hillside. Kim frowned, her heart going out to it, and involuntarily she turned to Vidas and said with a touch of anger, 'Why are you people of the East so cruel to your animals?'

Startled by the vehemence of her outburst, he seemed unable to reply at once. When he did, it was to say curiously, 'Does it trouble you so much, then?'

'It would trouble anyone with a heart!'

'Are you suggesting we of the East don't have hearts?' His footsteps slowed, then stopped. Kim drew her hand away, then wished she hadn't.

'Have you no imagination to understand the suffering of that poor little donkey up there? He's probably thirsty, and in addition his food is out of his reach.'

'Food?' he echoed enquiringly.

'The grass. He'll have eaten all that is within reach.'

'That's one reason for tethering an animal—to prevent it from eating too much.'

'It's no use trying to make you understand,' she said impatiently, then fell silent. For an idea had occurred to her, and when Vidas was taking a stroll a couple of days later, he stopped in amazement at seeing a bedraggled little donkey grazing in a newly made paddock in a rather remote part of the castle grounds.

'Where the devil did that donkey come from?' he demanded, after striding back to the patio where he knew his wife was sitting, clad in bright green shorts and a scanty white sun top that left little to the imagination.

'Him . . . ? Oh, I bought him—'

'Bought him?' He cut her off, his eyebrows raised. It was plain that he suspected she had taken leave of her senses. 'Are you serious?'

'Of course.'

'What on earth did you buy him for?'

'To rescue him,' replied Kim, having regained her calm after the slight shock Vidas had given her by speaking so sharply and in that imperious tone of voice. 'He needed to be rescued, don't you think? Have you seen how thin he is?'

Vidas eyed her narrowly. 'Do you intend to buy every donkey you hear complaining of its lot?'

'I might buy a few more,' she stated, closing her book with slow deliberation and leaning forward to place it on the rattan table in front of her. 'There's plenty of room for more paddocks back there, close to where Rocky is. Nothing's ever been done to that part of the castle grounds. I know because I asked Sula. He said that in all the years he's been head gardener here that part of the grounds has always been wild. It could be used as a sort of animal sanctuary, a haven for ill-treated donkeys and perhaps dogs.'

'Did it not occur to you to seek my permission before embarking on this . . . er . . . rescue scheme?' The voice was taut and yet Kim sensed an undercurrent of amused tolerance. There was an indulgent quality about the expression in his eyes, too, despite their narrowed scrutiny.

'I didn't think you'd mind my taking over that waste ground for my new hobby.'

'Hobby? So you're serious about this ridiculous business?'

'It's not a ridiculous business,' she denied hotly. 'It's a human duty to save animals from suffering.'

A sigh of exasperation followed her spirited words before Vidas spoke again, and when he did it was to point out that, not only would the donkey she had bought be replaced by another, but once the news of her activities spread through the local community, every peasant for miles around would start mistreating his donkey in the hope of getting her to buy it.

'Prices will go up and up until you'll be spending every drachma of your allowance buying donkeys—' He broke off and gave a gust of laughter. 'Kim, you're the limit!'

His humour was contagious and Kim found herself laughing too, but there was no weakening of her determination to start an animal sanctuary on the castle grounds.

'You won't object to my using that land, will you?' she asked, and for a long moment her gaze became anxious because, in spite of her resolve, she did have to regard her husband's wishes. He would certainly see to that!

'I suppose not,' he answered at length, an incomprehensible smile curving his lips. 'But do you expect me to supply the materials and labour for all the fencing you are going to need?'

Her lashes fluttered and a winning smile appeared. She saw his eyes narrow but feigned ignorance of his perception as she said, quietly and at her most persuasive, 'If you would provide the labour, Vidas, I'd be very grateful. The fencing won't cost anything because Sula cut trees from the forest for the paddock he and the others made this morning.'

'He and the others?' with a lift of his eyebrows. 'So all my employees have been engaged on the paddock instead of the gardens?'

'Well . . . er . . . yes.'

'I'm beginning to think,' said Vidas in strong, decisive tones, 'that there are parts unknown about you

119

that I ought to be investigating.' She said nothing and
he added, after a pause, 'What exactly are you trying to
do?'

'Do?' she repeated, puzzled by the sudden glint in his
eyes. 'Are you vexed with me?' Little did she know just
how appealing she looked, how young and artless, as
she stood still, staring at him with wide questioning
eyes, her mind disturbed by the incomprehensible
change in his attitude towards her, the amused tolerance of a few moments ago having given place to an
impatience that bordered on anger.

He gave a small sigh and said, 'No, I am not vexed
with you.'

She looked at him, musing on what he had been
saying these last few minutes, and suddenly her eyes
widened. *He was fighting against falling in love with
her.* He had stressed his aversion to becoming emotionally involved with a woman, but despite this, he was
now finding her attractive in other ways than the purely
physical. There were parts unknown about her, he had
said . . . and he ought to be investigating them. . . .
But he had then asked her what she was trying to do.
And there had been anger in his voice. Perception
dawned again and Kim realised that he suspected her of
trying to make him fall in love with her. He believed
this concern for animals was part of a plan to reveal
certain attractive traits, which, added up, would in the
end pierce all his defences. But he was a hard man; he
would fight against anything that did not appeal to
him . . . and loving a woman did not appeal to him. He
was convinced that emotional entanglement was de-
structive to a man; with his typical, Greek view of
things, he had decided that love did not last, and
therefore he considered it futile even to think about it.

But Kim, with her woman's intuition, knew he *was* thinking about it—oh, not consciously, she felt sure! But he was becoming both angry and bewildered by his feelings for her. Well, she thought with satisfaction, he had given her a weapon she would be a fool not to use. He was vulnerable after all, and it was up to her to make a concerted effort to weaken his defences even more, to the point where the last shred of armour was stripped from him.

Chapter Nine

The following day she wandered along a narrow lane, admiring the gleaming white cubic houses whose gardens smouldered with brilliant colour from hibiscus and oleander, bougainvillaea vines and passion flowers. On every patio there was an assortment of earthenware pots, petrol cans, and other improbable containers all bright with flowers growing in them and tumbling over their sides. In the hedgerows between the houses pomegranate flowers, crimson and gaudy, flaunted their beauty in the sunshine. Mountains soared, dark against the blue, and the gracious castle belonging to Bridie's husband stood gleaming and mellowed on its jutting cliff. All was quiet but for the drone of insects and the distant laughter of children. No crying babies. Kim had never once heard a baby cry since she came to Malindos, and often she had wondered why Greek babies should be more contented than those of her own country. She had mentioned this to Adela once and was told of the great love and affection the Greeks have for their children.

'They'd never be left to cry,' stated Adela, 'and so you never hear them.'

And yet, thought Kim, as the bray of a donkey reached her ears, they cared nothing at all for their animals. It was a case of: it's only a donkey. Why should you worry whether or not a donkey is happy?

Kim wandered on, responding to the occasional *Kalimera, Kyria Vidas!'*

'*Kalimera*—good morning to you.'

At first she had found it strange that she should be addressed as Mrs. Vidas and had mentioned it to her husband. It was the custom in Greece, he told her, for a woman to be called by her husband's Christian name.

The donkey was troubling her, and although she had decided she could not possibly buy every donkey on the island, she found herself turning into a lane, which led her to where the unfortunate animal was tethered, on a piece of ground quite bare of vegetation. The sun was rising in the heavens; the atmosphere was unbearably hot. The donkey began to paw the ground, sending up a cloud of dust into which its nose descended as he looked for food. She frowned as she went towards it. There was a deep cut on its head which, to her horror, was completely covered with flies. She looked around and noticed a well with a battered pail beside it. The donkey cried pitifully, and she filled the bucket and took it to him, watching as he drank thirstily until there was scarcely a drop left.

'What do you do with my donkey?'

Kim swung round so swiftly that she almost hit the ill-clad, stocky Greek in the chest with the bucket. 'This animal belongs to you?' she said wrathfully.

'It is my donkey, yes. You haf no right to give my water to him! Water is scarce! It not rain for two-three weeks!'

Kim threw down the pail and drew herself up, eyes glinting. 'Have you ever been dying of thirst?' she asked.

He gave the typical shrug of the Greek peasant. It was as much a part of his general makeup as the gold fillings and the worry beads he was twirling at his side.

'I been thirsty—yes.' He paused momentarily, regarding her with a curious expression, 'You on holiday, madam?'

'I'm Mrs. Vidas Christou—'

'You—!' His manner changed, a self-deprecating smile touching his lips. 'You Mrs. Vidas. Welcome to our island! Mr. Vidas, he good to my son who hurt—injured—what you say?—in the sea.'

'Your son's a sponge diver?'

'Once he the best on this island. But one day he caught in the deep current and they bring him up paralysed. Mr. Vidas he give him money every week for his wife and children. Mr. Vidas very good man!'

Her interest fully caught, Kim forgot the donkey for a space as she asked more questions about the sponge divers who were once so numerous on this and the surrounding islands. She learnt that the men would carry a massive boulder to increase their speed of descent to the bottom where, with a long knife, they would slash at the sponges in the urgent knowledge that time was not on their side. They were paid for the sponges by dry weight. Kim learnt that the ships used to go out from the harbour every spring, and there was a ceremony on board when the priests would go around everything with the holy water, murmuring blessings all the time, while the whole community gathered on the waterfront to pray for the safety of the men they would not see again for the next five months. The coast of Africa was one of the most lucrative fishing grounds, but many men had come home from there crippled for life.

'And now there are not many sponge divers?' she asked, when the man stopped speaking.

'Not many, but those who still go, they haf this new things—what you call equip—equip . . . ?'

'Equipment,' supplied Kim, her eyes wandering to the donkey, now braying again and pawing the ground.

'Yes, that is it. But they haf no courage—bah! The old way was good!'

'It couldn't have been,' argued Kim shortly. 'The men's lives were in danger the whole time they were in the water.'

The man said nothing and Kim turned to look at the gash on the donkey's head.

'How did that happen?' she demanded, her manner changing to one of sternness again.

'I hit him to make him go,' answered the man casually. 'He very stubborn, that cretur! He haf a will of his own that I shall break!'

'Does it occur to you that the donkey might respond to kindness?'

'Respond?' with a wrinkling of his low forehead. 'What is this respond?'

She gave a sigh of asperity and determined to take lessons in Greek. 'How much do you want . . . er . . . what is your name?'

'Elias, I haf other name—'

'Elias, will you sell me your donkey?'

'You want to buy Mitso?' He looked at her as if suspecting her of making some sort of a joke. 'You not want Mitso—'

'How much?' she cut in, shuddering at the idea of all those flies sucking the unfortunate animal's blood. 'I do want to buy your donkey. How much?'

'But—'

'Elias,' she said impatiently, 'how much do you want for Mitso?'

'Is it Mr. Vidas who wants him?' The man still seemed as if he suspected Kim of pulling his leg, this despite the frowning countenance she turned upon him.

'No . . .' She allowed her voice to trail away to silence as an idea occurred to her. If this man thought Vidas wanted the donkey, then undoubtedly he would let him have it at a fair price. 'Yes, as a matter of fact it is my husband who wants to buy your donkey.'

'But why?'

'He . . . er . . .' Kim racked her brain. 'He's collecting them,' she said, producing a smile.

The man's black eyes widened to their fullest extent. 'Collecting donkeys?' Elias shook his head. 'You—what they say?—you take me for—for fool and laugh at me.'

Kim drew an exasperated breath. 'How much will you sell Mitso for?' she persisted. 'My husband really does want to buy him.'

The man stood there, nonplussed, as well he might be, faced with a situation that made him wonder if he were dreaming. But at last he spoke, stating a price which, compared with what she had paid for Rocky, was reasonable.

'Bring him up to the castle at once and you will be paid,' she said, and walked swiftly away before Elias could ask any more questions.

Two hours later she was cleaning the wound while Sula held the animal's head and repeatedly exchanged glances with Kimon, one of the other gardeners who stood by, glances that plainly said that their new mistress was more than a little mad.

'The ointment, Sula,' she said, and he stepped forward to hand her the jar. 'You say there is not a veterinary surgeon on this island?' She looked at him as she took the jar and unscrewed the lid.

'No, Madam Vidas, we have no animal doctor here.'

'What happens when an animal is ill?'

'We send to Rhodes for animal doctor.'

'The animal might die because of the delay.'

Sula shrugged his shoulders and said, 'It is only an animal, madam.'

'You all need to learn some lessons!' she snapped, digging her finger into the jar. She applied the ointment thickly, as much as a barrier against the flies as a healing balm to the actual wound itself. 'Now, put him in with Rocky and then set about making another paddock—a very large one this time!'

'So you've bought another one already.' It was several hours later that Vidas made the observation, coming upon Kim when, having phoned Bridie, she had just replaced the receiver on its rest.

'You've seen Mitso? Did you notice the dreadful cut on his head?'

Vidas's lips twitched. 'No one could miss it, my dear.' His manner, appearing to be indulgent, encouraged Kim to ask about having a vet take up practice on the island.

'We don't have much need for a vet,' he returned, but there was that about him which spelled resignation —or nearly so, and Kim's spirits rose.

'If I am to have an animal sanctuary, then I must be able to call on the services of a vet,' she pointed out. 'Can you arrange to have an advertisement put into the newspapers? We might have to bring one from Athens, mightn't we?'

'What makes you suppose I'm in agreement with your having a vet living on Malindos?'

'One is needed,' she said persuasively. 'We have dogs here, and surely some people have horses?'

'One or two do. The Grivases ride, but George seems to be very capable of looking after his horses himself.'

'I can have a vet, can't I?' Kim slanted him a glance from under incredibly long lashes, saw his eyes glint as if he knew full well she was flirting with him. But for all that, she persevered, giving him a lovely smile which she hoped was reflected in her eyes. 'It's a wonderful hobby, looking after animals,' she said softly. 'You wouldn't want me to be bored, would you, Vidas?'

'I ought to slap you,' he murmured, and yet there was a gleam of amusement in his eyes.

'You must admit that Mitso was desperately unhappy.'

'What a name for a donkey! And what about Rocky? That's not Greek.'

'I called him Rocky because he was so weak he actually rocked on his legs, and at first I thought he was going to collapse altogether.'

'You're too softhearted, Kim. Donkeys are the hardiest animals alive.'

Ignoring this, Kim broached the subject of the vet, and a wave of satisfaction swept through her when Vidas agreed to advertise for one in the Athens newspapers. But he did ask who was going to pay the vet's salary.

'He'll set up an independent practise,' was her confident reply and Vidas's brows shot up.

'It's plain that you do not know what our peasant community is like. This vet will get little or no business from people like Elias. They'd never spend their drachmae that way. As for the more well-to-do residents, there are so few of us that he'd not get much that way either.' He made a gesture with his hand. 'Apart from these donkeys you're bent on befriending, there aren't many animals on the island.'

'There are plenty of dogs.'

'And they're all so hardy that they never require a vet.'

'Oh, dear . . .' A deep sigh escaped Kim before she said, tilting her lovely face to look up into his, 'Will you pay his salary, Vidas?'

To her surprise he laughed. 'I wondered when you'd get round to what you had in mind right at the start—'

'Oh, no, I really thought he'd be able to build up a practice.'

'I'll pay his salary,' offered Vidas with a sigh, and then, after a pause during which his face changed and a sternness brought a glint to his eye and a rigidity to his mouth, 'If I don't end up beating you, my girl, it'll be a miracle!'

When he had gone, Kim smiled to herself. She was making progress . . . and the chief thought in her mind at this moment was certainly not the animal sanctuary she meant to have.

Birdie came by the following morning in response to Kim's request over the telephone. 'What's all this about an animal sanctuary?" she asked eagerly, almost before she had sat down on the patio. "I could hardly wait to get here to learn more about it! As I told you, I'm keenly interested in charity work, and for a long while I've been troubled about the cruelty to animals I have come across here, but the idea of starting a sanctuary never occurred to me! Yes, I am willing to join you, and yes, I agree that we ought to have a body equivalent to the ASPCA. I can get a few helpers and I feel we ought to drag in our husbands, don't you?'

'I'm working on it," admitted Kim on an impish note. 'Vidas is willing to pay for me to bring a vet to the island.'

Strangely, Bridie was not surprised. She said, in the soft Irish brogue that Kim found so very charming and attractive, 'He's a wonderful man—always willing to give to charity. I don't approach him myself because I'm not the secretary of our organisation, but I do know that he would never refuse to help any charity. And what he's done for the maimed sponge divers is fantastic. He must spend a small fortune every year on helping them and their families.'

A wonderful man . . . Yes, Kim was fast learning that her original opinion of him was exceedingly false, but then she could be excused, she told herself, because his attitude towards her had been hateful, to say the least.

She and Bridie talked over coffee and biscuits, making plans to ensure that every animal on the island would be treated humanely in the future.

'Vidas says that once it's known that I'm buying donkeys, the price will soar.' Kim and Bridie had wandered from the patio to the remote part of the grounds where Mitso and Rocky were contentedly grazing amidst the lush green grass. The animals were in the shade of a huge banyan tree, and close to the hedge was a trough filled with clean water. Not far away, Sula and Kimon were putting stakes in the ground, which the other two gardeners were busy clearing of rough scrub and rotting vegetation.

'And he's right! But you just phone me and I'll come with you when you want to buy. I've lived here longer than you and know how to handle these simple country people. They'll fleece you if they can, yet they'd give you their last drachma if you had nothing. A complex race, the Greeks, especially the island people, who are remote from places like Athens. I'll be able to bargain with them.'

'I did manage very well over both Rocky and Mitso,' Kim had to say. 'I was very stern with Elias, and we shall be able to be sterner still once we've set up this protection society. Vidas says quite logically that every donkey I buy will be replaced by another. However, if we threaten the owners with prosecution, then they're going to take more care, aren't they?'

'Yes, and that means we won't have to buy so many of the animals.'

'We?'

'I'm in on this, Kim—wouldn't miss it for anything!

George will give me some money for a cause such as ours.'

Both girls were excited about the project, and when, a fortnight later, a young Englishman, Denis Studland, took up residence as the veterinary surgeon on the island, they were even more excited because, having lived on another island and been appalled by the cruelty, he was as enthusiastic as they about their plans.

One thing troubled Kim, however. From the moment of meeting her, Denis had been interested in her as a woman. It was something he found impossible to hide and even Bridie had noticed it.

'I hope no complications set in,' she said one day, when she and Kim had been on a visit to Denis, who lived in a pretty little blue and white villa a few hundred yards back from the island's loveliest beach. They had gone to discuss the setting up of the protection society and had stayed rather longer than they had intended because he had persuaded them to have afternoon tea with him. And as they were leaving he actually put his arm around Kim's shoulders and asked if she would come the following morning and join him for a swim. She made the excuse that her husband would expect her to swim with him, as usual, and Denis's disappointment could be felt. Vidas had never asked Kim to swim with him, but on occasion they had met at the pool and spent a few minutes together in the water, so she felt that what she had told Denis was only a white lie.

'I hope so, too,' was her fervent response to her friend's comment. 'He's so nice, and we all get along so well together that it would be a shame if anything went wrong at this stage.'

'Well, he's certainly smitten, Kim.' A pause followed

because Kim did not speak. 'I should imagine from what little I know of your husband that he could be violently jealous—but I expect you will have gathered that already?'

'No,' murmured Kim thoughtfully, 'as a matter of fact, I haven't . . . but there has never been an occasion where he could be jealous.'

'There is now, though.'

'Yes,' agreed Kim in the same quiet tone of voice, 'there is now. . . .'

Was it fair to use Denis in order to make Vidas jealous? Perhaps Bridie was mistaken and Vidas would not be jealous—Kim stopped the thought, for she knew instinctively that he would be wildly jealous—not because he loved her but simply because she was his property, body and soul, as he had once told her. He would definitely be jealous if he thought another man was interested in her . . . and she interested in him. And as it was true that there could be no jealousy without love, it was reasonable to assume that Vidas would eventually realise that he did love his wife, that his defences were broken and he might as well accept his fate.

As the days went by and Kim's plans began to materialise, she found her thoughts straying again to the idea of making her husband jealous. In her attempt to win his love she had flirted with him, had tried to bewilder him by adopting a clinging air of mystery, noting his reaction and silently laughing at his angry bafflement. He now knew, of course, that there was nothing really bad about her, had learnt that all his previous guesses had been wrong. But she suspected that at this stage he would be more willing to find faults in her than otherwise, simply because he could then

133

convince himself that he was right in fighting against falling in love with her. But Kim was determined never to let him see any faults; at present she was on the attack and he on the defensive, and she was striving to keep it that way, even while knowing it was a situation he plainly hated and was endeavouring to combat. In short, she was determined to make him fall in love with her, and he equally determined to fight every move she made. The idea of using Denis in order to make Vidas jealous, however, was not really acceptable to her, because Denis was a nice sort who didn't deserve to be hurt.

Could she use him without hurting him, though? Kim felt she could, and one evening at dinner she looked across at her husband and said, 'Can we have Denis over for a meal one evening, Vidas? He's a little lost here, with no friends yet. And he's such a charming man—but I've no need to tell you that, have I? You've met him several times.'

Vidas looked at her darkly. 'I didn't find him particularly charming,' he said brusquely.

'No?' with raised eyebrows and a surprised look in eyes that became wide and large. 'But, Vidas, everyone thinks he's great!'

'Everyone? I thought he didn't know anybody?'

A slip! She said with a smile, 'He's met the people who are interested in our scheme—they're mainly people Bridie comes into contact with in her charity work.'

Vidas picked up the silver basket containing crispy rolls and held it out to her, his eyes never leaving her face. Unpredictable man! What was he thinking behind those hooded, foreign eyes?

'You have an answer for everything, my dear,' he

said smoothly. 'Yes, of course we must ask your friend to dinner. I leave it to you to make the arrangements.' A seconds pause and then, 'To make a foursome we could ask a friend of mine.'

'Of—yours?' Something tightened in the region of Kim's stomach. 'Wh-who is it?'

'A certain Floria Costalos. She's a distant cousin of George Grivas. She and I were rather more than friendly this time last year.'

'You were?'

'Yes. My stepmother almost drove me to marriage.' Another fractional pause ensued. 'Didn't Bridie mention anything about Floria?'

'No . . . er . . . yes, I seem to remember something —I wasn't taking much notice at the time.'

'You weren't?' with a sort of mocking scepticism. 'Are you quite sure?'

'Is there any reason why I should lie?' she challenged.

'Shall we change the subject?' he suggested gently. 'Tell me how many donkeys you have now.'

The colour that had risen in her face subsided as her cool composure returned. 'Seven—but two of them were bought by George, Bridie's husband.'

'So Bridie has dragged him in, has she?'

'We have several people interested now. The protection society has been voted a necessity and already we have four people who are willing to give their services free. They'll each have an area to patrol—when they have time, that is,' she added swiftly, on seeing Vidas's brows lift in surprised enquiry. 'They'll report any mishandling of animals, be they horses, donkeys, dogs, or cats.'

'You have a system, then?'

'Of course.'

'And how do you suppose the people here are going to take to this interference in their lives?'

'They'll get used to it, and we're hoping that when Denis has given his series of lectures, the small farmers especially will be better informed as to how their donkeys should be treated.'

Vidas laughed, but when she asked outright for the money to buy a building that could be used as a sort of dispensary, he agreed at once to provide it, rather to her surprise in light of the turn the conversation had taken. 'It's an animal hospital you want, I presume?'

'In a way.' Kim gave him a disarming smile, half-prepared for what was to come.

'So, in effect, you require much more than the building.' Again that quirk of amusement on his lips. 'Why prolong both your own agony and mine by asking for small sums of money? You'd best come out with the whole amount and let me consider it.'

A smile fluttered again, brightening her face, lighting her beautiful eyes. 'You're good and generous,' she said. 'I do appreciate what you are doing for a cause in which you basically have no interest. It's very commendable,' she added finally.

Vidas's face was a mask of unresponsiveness as he murmured softly, 'You're very transparent. Flattery is lost on me, my dear, so you needn't waste your time extending it.'

She coloured delicately, and then the tension was relieved as they both burst into laughter.

'Will you really equip the dispensary?' she asked.

'I might. Depends on how much it's going to cost.'

With the help of Denis and Bridie, the cost was

estimated and presented to Vidas in an envelope, which he took, regarding his wife with a faintly sardonic smile. But he paid up, and as there was no paucity of labour on the island, the building was up and equipped in less than a fortnight. Meanwhile, the dinner party was arranged and Floria, having come to stay with George and Bridie, arrived in George's car. Kim would have liked to have George and Bridie as well, but they had other visitors, and although Kim would have included them, Bridie said it would be nicer to have an intimate dinner later, just the four of them.

Floria turned out to be even more attractive than Kim had imagined from the description given her by Bridie. Tall and dark, with clear golden skin and deep-set eyes that looked green in one light and the deepest grey in another, Floria Costalos was a woman who would attract attention wherever she went. Her movements were smooth and dignified, her manner of speaking that of a woman who was both fascinating and highly intelligent. Her eyes raked Kim's figure in an almost malignant way, but the smile she produced was all charm and good nature, and the words she uttered cleverly designed to dispel any doubts Kim might have had as to her sincerity.

'How nice to meet Vidas's wife at last! I wish you every happiness, Kim. What a charming name! Is it short for anything?'

'No, I was christened Kim.' The hand she held out was steady, cool. 'I'm delighted to meet you.'

Vidas looked on after making the introductions, an enigmatic smile hovering on his face. Denis arrived within five minutes of Floria and almost immediately the four of them were engaged in conversation, sipping aperitifs on the patio, with dusk descending to send shadows, turret-shaped, across the smooth, velvet lawn. Water from a fountain made music to mingle with the whirr of cicadas, and perfumes floated on the air, mingling with the more potent tang of the sea. Kim lifted her head to allow the breeze to caress her face; it tousled her hair, and she saw Denis's eyes become fixed upon this sight for a few unfathomable seconds before moving to her face, when a slow smile broke, to which she responded, profoundly conscious of both Floria and Vidas looking at her with interest.

'I suppose,' said Vidas into the lull in the conversation, 'that Bridie has told you about the activities that are going on regarding the comfort of the animals on this island?'

Floria nodded and her mouth made a grimace of amusement. 'I expect it's something that will die a natural death. You can't dictate to a Greek peasant like that. He is not going to take any heed at all.'

Kim and Denis exchanged glances, and noticing this, Floria gave Kim an arch stare.

'It's no temporary thing,' Denis said firmly. 'We intend to establish a certain code of behaviour regarding the treatment of all animals here on Malindos.'

'An idealistic notion,' laughed Floria, eyes on the liquid in her glass. 'But you are dealing with people who live by custom rather than law. To impose law will antagonise them and they'll deliberately flout it—just for their own satisfaction.'

Kim was faintly troubled by these words, but had no intention of allowing Vidas's ex-girl friend to see it. 'If they flout the law they will be fined.'

'But you are not the law,' she pointed out. 'Why

should anyone like you, who has only recently come to live here, be so presumptuous as to assume you can inflict your ideas on a people who, as I've said, live by custom?'

'We intend to proceed in the face of any opposition,' put in Denis quietly. 'On another island—Cyprus, in fact—there is a body of young women who have formed an animal protection society and it's most successful—or was, the last time I spoke to one of the women.'

Floria shrugged her elegant shoulders. 'Time alone will tell if you can succeed. Personally, I feel the whole scheme's doomed to failure.' She turned to Vidas. 'What do you think about it?' she asked, her dark eyes flickering over his face, absorbing every impressive feature.

Kim's mouth compressed, for there was something savouring of the possessive in the Greek girl's attitude towards her old flame. Perhaps, mused Kim with a stab of spite, she was a woman who did not easily give up, and this invitation of Vidas's must surely have made her feel he really wanted to see her again. Kim was suddenly angry with her husband, and in her anger she turned all her attention to Denis, whose arm had somehow come to rest across the back of her chair.

'I have nothing to do with the project,' said Vidas, in reply to Floria's question. 'My role in all this seems to be that of financier.'

'You mean you do all the paying out?' Floria stared disbelievingly at him. 'But, surely you have more sense than to finance something that is bound to fail?'

Kim's eyes glittered. 'It is not bound to fail!' she said through her teeth. She was still a trifle worried, but still determined to hide her fears. The trouble was that this girl's personality, strong like Vidas's, seemed in some vexing way to overwhelm Kim. Floria had an elastic spring to her speech and a vitality about the way she threw her words together that seemed calculated to render Kim's own manner of speaking colourless. It was humiliating, and when Kim was humiliated anger was the result.

And so the meal was by no means as pleasant as it ought to have been; the conversation kept reverting to the project even though both Kim and Denis tried to veer it towards other channels. And all the while Vidas looked on, contributing very little, just sitting there, appearing to enjoy his wife's growing discomfiture.

She was determined to get her own back, and as soon as the meal was over she said sweetly, 'Perhaps, Vidas, you and Floria would like to be left to talk over old times? Denis and I have things to discuss regarding the dispensary, so if you'll excuse us . . . ?' Her voice trailed off; she trembled a little at her husband's expression but at the same time felt elated that she had managed to shake him out of his indifferent manner.

Denis was looking oddly at her, wondering what she was about. She slipped her arm through his and, with another request to be excused, steered him to the open French window. They were through it before Kim heard Floria say, 'Well, that was obliging of her. . . .'

'What's the game?' Denis wanted to know once they were away from the window. 'You have me puzzled, Kim.'

'Sorry, Denis.' She stopped to draw a long breath. 'I couldn't have stood that girl a moment longer. You didn't mind my suggesting we come out here, did you, Denis?'

'Indeed no! I shall be very happy to stroll in the moonlight with you.'

She laughed lightly. 'What shall we discuss?' she asked, withdrawing her arm from his.

'Nothing—at least, nothing to do with the project.'

'The building's going up according to plan? There's nothing you think should be altered? We don't want to discover, afterwards, that we ought to have done it differently.'

'The design of the building's so simple that we can make interior alterations as and when they are necessary.' They had reached the darkness of the olive trees and he stopped, 'Kim . . .'

'Yes?'

'You and Vidas—I mean, tonight, you didn't act like a honeymoon couple.'

'We're not on our honeymoon.'

'You know what I mean,' he said a trifle impatiently. 'And that woman—Floria—there was something strange going on between her and your husband. He never made a move to stop her when she was deriding our project, treating it with scorn.'

'They're old flames,' she told him, feeling that Bridie would probably mention the fact anyway. 'Vidas was on the point of marrying her this time last year.'

'So there *was* something.' Denis shook his head, an angry gesture, though the expression in his eyes was all puzzlement. 'Are you in love with your husband?' he demanded bluntly.

'Very much in love,' she replied.

'Then he—? I can't think he's in love with you, Kim. He didn't act in any way as if he were. There was never a sign of tenderness, never a glance such as one would expect from a man so recently married. And the way he was with Floria—almost siding with her against you—'

'No such thing,' protested Kim hotly. 'That is not true, Denis!'

'Well, he didn't side with you! Nor did he put a stop to her jeering!'

That was so and Kim could not deny it. 'Floria was his guest, remember, so he couldn't say much—'

'He didn't say anything! I don't care what you say, Kim, there's something not quite right about you and your husband. Why, if you knew he and she had been on the point of marriage only a year ago, did you come out here and leave them alone? It isn't logical.'

True again, but how could she tell him that her action had been spurred partly by anger and partly by the hope that Vidas would be jealous?

'I wanted to come out into the air,' she said. 'I've already told you that I couldn't stand the girl a moment longer.'

'That's the point! You dislike her and yet you leave her in there, alone with your husband.' Denis shook his head, baffled and angry. 'Kim,' he said after a long pause in which Kim had made to walk on again until he grabbed hold of her arm, 'you must be aware of how I feel about you—'

'Please, Denis,' she broke in, distressed. 'I spoke the truth when I said I love my husband.'

'Does he love you?' he challenged. She did not answer and he added on a note of triumph, 'You'd like to lie but you find you can't. He isn't in love with you, but that's nothing new with his kind! I've lived in Greece long enough to know that few Greek men marry for love. On, Kim, what made you marry him?'

'I'm not willing to go into it,' she returned, her words stiff and cold. 'I suggest we go back.' She blamed herself for all this, and rightly so. What would happen now? Would Denis abandon the scheme and leave the island? Oh, why had she acted so impulsively? Just because she was furious with her husband and even more furious with his ex-girl friend. She put a hand on Denis's arm and said gently, 'You'll not give up this project, will you, Denis?'

'I don't know,' he answered bitterly. 'How can I keep on seeing you, feeling as I do? If I leave now it will be bad enough, but if I stay it's going to be worse. . . .' His voice trailed away into silence as he became thoughtful. 'Perhaps your marriage will break up, and if so—'

'It'll never break up,' she assured him. 'Vidas would never hear of a separation.'

'And you? Are you willing to live with a man who doesn't love you?'

'I've said I'm not willing to discuss my marriage. I want you to stay—if only until we get the whole thing organised. We need an experienced man, and if you leave we could be weeks or even months finding someone else. You were the only one who answered the advertisement, and we now know that the post we were offering would not appeal to most people. They want something far more lucrative—they want a practise of their own where they have an opportunity of making a lot of money.'

'With me it is a calling—if you care to accept it as that. I was intrigued by the advertisement, and once I'd met you and Bridie, I was fired with enthusiasm and the salary was of secondary importance.'

'I believe you,' said Kim, and a sigh escaped her. 'You are just the man for the job, Denis, so please don't do anything impulsive, will you?'

'I'll stay for a while,' he promised, after a moment of consideration.

'Thank you,' she said simply, and turned with the intention of going back to the castle. But suddenly she was caught around the waist, and feeling she was losing her balance, she clung to the lapels of his coat. The next moment she felt the hard pressure of his mouth on hers, and stunned into immobility, she just stood there, trying to collect her thoughts.

'What the devil—!' Her husband's voice, snarling and harsh, brought Kim back with a jerk, her heart leaping into her throat. She was free of Denis's hold, dragged away by Vidas in his rage. She saw the two men facing one another, and without waiting another second, she plunged away into the darkness, running towards the side door of the castle through which she and Denis had come only a few minutes before.

Chapter Ten

Kim stood before the open window of her bedroom, her heart beating furiously. What had she done by her impulsive act in inviting Denis to go outside with her? What was happening now? She realised that Floria must have come out onto the grounds with Vidas. She had caught a glimpse of a dark shape in the shadows, which must have been the Greek girl, who was probably gloating as she watched Vidas's wrathful action on seeing his wife in another man's arms.

It was perhaps a quarter of an hour later that a sound caught Kim's ears and she wheeled swiftly from the window, conscious of quiet, hurried footsteps. For the next few seconds she suffered the skin-prickling sensation of waiting for the bedroom door to open, which it did, with a violence that sent it crashing into a wardrobe, then back again to be kicked shut by the heel of her husband's shoe. He stood there, eyes smouldering, his face a twisted mask of pagan fury. Her frightened eyes were drawn to his lean brown hands, clenching and unclenching at his sides . . . and one of her own hands stole quiveringly to her throat.

'Vidas—I . . .' She tried to speak even though she had no idea what to say, and in any case her mouth was so dry she could scarcely articulate. 'You're angry, but—'

'Angry!' He strode towards her with purpose in every stride. 'Humiliated, more like! How dare you show me up!' He stopped close, to tower above her, a menacing figure from which Kim would have fled if she could.

'Humiliation . . .' For a fleeting moment that was all that registered in her mind. She had set out to make him jealous, in the hope that he would discover he loved her. All she had done was to humiliate him, and it was this, and not jealousy, which had created his fury. It had all been a waste, a vain effort.

'Yes, humiliation! That little scene will be talked about from one end of this island to the other by this time tomorrow! And it will be magnified over and over again until the gossips will have you and Studland lying on the ground making—'

'Stop!' she lashed out, all fear dissolving in the heat of her own rising anger. 'Who is going to start this gossip, anyway?'

'Floria, who else—?'

'Floria . . .' Yes, for spite! 'But she cannot say that Denis and I were—were doing anything wrong. . . .' Or could she?'

'The gossips will do the exaggerating!' For a moment he was so consumed by wrath that he seemed to have difficulty in speaking. 'How long has this affair been going on?' he demanded, and before she could answer he had gripped her arms, ruthlessly crushing them, making her wince as she uttered a cry of protest, which was instantly cut off as he began shaking her unmercifully, shaking her till her teeth chattered and her hair fell in wild disorder about her tear-stained face. A plea was turned into a sharp cry of pain as her tongue became trapped between her teeth. 'I ought to strangle you!' he thundered. 'I warned you long ago that if ever you did anything to besmirch my good name you'd suffer, and why I don't make you smart I don't know!'

Released at last, Kim swayed on legs that seemed to have lost their ability to support her. Vidas caught her, propelled her roughly towards the bed and flung her onto it.

'I hate you,' she whispered, managing to sit up. 'You're a savage.'

'Don't try me too far,' he said through gritted teeth, standing there, glowering at her and ready to do her further injury, she thought, as she put soothing fingers to the places on her arms where she knew there must be bruises. 'How long has this affair been going on?' he asked again.

'It is not an affair—'

'Don't lie! What kind of a fool do you take me for? You and he went out there to make love—'

'We did not!' she stuck in. 'I was intending to talk business!'

'Business!' A harsh and gutteral sound escaped the depths of his throat. Kim likened it to the low and warning growl of a jungle beast preparing for the kill. She shivered, edging to one side of the bed as she tried to rise. She was helped by her husband, whose hand shot out to grip her wrist. The next moment she was crushed against the hard muscles of his body and her chin was tilted back, so that she felt as if her neck was being broken. For a long moment Vidas held her like this, watching, with a sort of evil satisfaction, the tears spiking her lashes, the convulsive twisting of her mouth. Then his lips closed on hers in a brutal, sensual kiss, which robbed her of breath for such an extended length of time that she was bordering on oblivion when at last he thought fit to give her air. Swaying, she clung to his arms, her frenzied fingers unconsciously digging into his flesh through the fine linen of his coat.

'It—it was to talk business, no—no matter wh-what you say. . . .' She was still in a semiconscious state, gulping for air between each word she uttered.

Vidas pushed her from him, onto the bed. 'I asked how long this affair has been going on. That little scene was proof enough that it had been going on for some time!'

Kim said nothing; she still wanted air in her lungs and she was inhaling spasmodically, hating Vidas for making her feel this way. Her neck was painful, her lips were bruised and swollen, and the terrible throbbing of her heart actually frightened her. 'I'm not having an affair with Denis,' she managed at last, lifting a white face to his, her tear-filled eyes examining his for signs that he believed her. She saw his lips curl, his eyes glint with scepticism and contempt.

'You lie!' he snarled. 'And so did he!'

'What d-did you do to—to him?' She faltered, managing to ask the question that had been in her mind all the time.

'I warned him to keep away from my wife! Also he's sacked!'

'Sacked? You mean—you're not willing to pay him his salary?'

A sneer caught her husband's underlip. 'Do you really expect me to pay the man a salary for making love to my wife?'

Kim's teeth snapped together and fire blazed in her eyes. 'That's a rotten, unthinking thing to say! You're so angry you've lost control of your reasoning as well as your temper—'

'I said he's sacked. There is to be no further argument on that score.' Implacable was the tone and hard the eyes that looked into hers.

A weight dropped down on her but she heard herself say, 'We need him and we're going to keep him!'

'You are? And how?'

'We'll find a way to pay him. Fortunately, he's dedicated, so it's possible that he'll work for less than you are giving him.'

Ignoring what she had said, Vidas told her harshly that her affair with Denis was at an end. 'At an end, do you understand?' he added menacingly. 'And by heaven, I shall watch you in the future!' On that parting shot he left her, trembling and tearful, still sitting on the bed.

In the ensuing silence she felt herself regain her calm; her heartbeats slowed to normal and her pulse and nerves began to settle. But she could not move because her stomach muscles seemed locked together, creating a sensation of physical sickness that she felt would increase if she rose to her feet. However, she did move at last, over an hour after Vidas had left her, and she went to the bathroom and ran the water. A bath was always soothing both to nerves and body, she had invariably found, and once she was lying in the scented water she was able to relax fully and to think clearly.

What a mess she had made of everything by obeying the angry impulse to invite Denis to go outside with her. All her plans had gone disastrously awry. She had lost the good opinion of her husband; it looked as if she had lost the services of Denis . . . and all she had gained were bruises. Would all her plans for the animal sanctuary and dispensary come to nothing? Kim felt sick at the idea of so much effort and no achievement.

When she came from the bathroom, clad only in the large bath sheet, it was to see her husband standing in his dressing gown by the window, his back to the room. She had come silently and was just stepping back into the bathroom when he turned.

'Come here!' he ordered harshly, his dark Greek eyes stripping the towel from her warm, powdered body. 'And make it quick if you don't want me to come to you!'

Kim was taking no risks. She went meekly to him, and for a moment their eyes locked. Wisely, she made no protest when he snatched the towel and flung it across the floor. His dressing gown was open and it was against her will that she glanced over his sinewy frame. It was as if her forced her to look before drawing her towards him, his hands warm and possessive as, with a familiar mastery, he spread his long lean fingers to press her quivering body close, moulding its supple lines to the hardness of his own.

His lips claimed hers, possessively, but to her surprise, not roughly, as she would have expected. After a while he held her at arms length, his sensual eyes moving over her gold-tinted body, darkening with amorous interest when they settled on the small white triangle that had been guarded from the sun.

'I suppose,' he said on a deliberately taunting note, 'that you are not in the mood for what I intend to do to you?'

'But you will do it nevertheless,' she returned stiffly.

'Of course. Haven't I said I own you . . . body and soul?'

'How typically Greek. Am I chattel, then?'

The dark eyes narrowed slightly. 'If you know the meaning of caution,' he said softly, 'then I'd advise you to regard it.'

'I do not think caution will serve any useful purpose at this stage,' she said.

'At this stage?' His eyes were drawn to the delicate contours of her breasts, and for a time he seemed far more interested in them than in the answer she gave him.

'You obviously intend to be revenged on me.'

Swiftly, he transferred his gaze to her wide, tear-misted eyes. 'You mean—you expect me to treat you roughly? What sort of a man do you think I am?'

Taken aback by the angry indignation in his voice, she frowned and said bewilderedly, 'You treated me roughly a few minutes ago and—'

'Not a few minutes ago,' he corrected. 'It's over an hour since I had the urge to make you smart.'

She swallowed convulsively. 'You're not angry any-more, then?'

'Shall we say—my anger has abated somewhat?'

'For any particular reason?' She grew warm under his

stare and watched his nostrils dilate as if he were vitally affected by the perfumed talc with which she had lavishly powdered herself.

'This is no time for talking,' he murmured, and there was a throaty bass inflection in his voice as, bending his head, he took her lips, moistly exploring, his tongue rough and masterful as it probed the warm darkness of her mouth. Fired as always by his caresses, Kim was soon in the throes of an uncontrollable excitement, her body heat rising to overcharge her heart and send the hot blood coursing through her veins. Vidas's body began to rock gently, and as she responded she felt herself to be on the heaving deck of a boat, exhilarated by a sort of sensual delirium of feeling. She quivered in every nerve cell when his experienced fingers, amorous on her breasts, brought the nipples to tingling peaks of desire. She was all his and he laughed softly in triumph when she gave a little muffled moan that was in reality a plea. Warm hands lifted her naked body; she was carried to the bed and laid there, while Vidas discarded his robe, watching her as he did so, noticing the alluring swell of her stomach, the rise and fall of breasts pulsating with life, ready for his possessive hands. Her mouth was parted, her hair a halo of glorious abandon, spread across the snowy whiteness of the pillow. He turned off the main light and all that was left was a small bedside light, its peach-tinted shade showering the room with a subtle, romantic glow—like twilight sprinkled with the rose-pink sheen left by the dying sun.

He lay down beside her. She felt the rippling muscles of his warm strong body as he brought her close, and with a low moan of contentment she abandoned herself in absolute surrender to the masterful demands he was about to make of her.

It was three days later that Vidas asked if Denis was leaving the island. 'I hope he has the sense to do so,' he added and lifted his eyebrows when Kim said no, Denis was not leaving.

'It's an unreasonable attitude on your part, Vidas. Why should he leave Malindos if he doesn't want to? You might own a good part of this island but you don't own it all, so you can't order people to leave. Denis has rented the villa for a year, with the option of a renewal. If he left now he'd have at least a year's rent to pay. In any case, I have persuaded him to stay.'

'I don't expect he needed much persuasion,' snapped Vidas, crimson threads of anger creeping up the sides of his mouth. 'Well, wife, I am now going to give an order that *will* be obeyed. You will resign from this idiotic organisation and give your attention to your duties here, in the castle.'

'I can't—I won't—!' There were tears in her eyes and a catch in her voice. 'It's my hobby, Vidas, and I *must* carry on with it!'

'And see that fellow every day?' He shook his head implacably. 'I forbid it!'

Anger brought colour to her cheeks. 'It's all a mistake,' she cried. 'There is nothing between Denis and me and you can't insist we don't work together!'

'I'm your husband and I shall see that you obey me.' His voice was very soft now, but the finality in its depths could not be missed. Furious with herself for putting herself in this position, Kim could almost have made a full confession, providing her husband with the

153

truth—that she had been trying to make him jealous. But after a moment's consideration she discarded the idea. She could not confess to a thing like that!

'Please, Vidas,' she begged, spreading her hands in an imploring little gesture, 'don't deny me this pleasure.' What would Bridie say? And the several other people who had succumbed to her persuasion and offered their services? It would look terrible if she were to resign. And what reason could she give if she did? But Vidas was adamant, and short of a rift Kim did not see how she was going to resolve her problem. 'Can I keep my own donkeys?' she asked at last.

'I have no objection to that,' he said, 'but don't buy any more.'

She bit her lip till it hurt. This whole situation was ridiculous, brought on as it was by her own stupidity. 'I suppose,' she said, 'I can visit Bridie?'

'I have no objections to that either.'

'Bridie's mixed up in it all.'

'She doesn't give all her time to it. See her socially.' He appeared bored suddenly, indifferent. 'I have work to do in my study,' he said. 'Just you do as I say and stay away from Studland.' And with that he left her, seething and frustrated, helpless to disentangle herself from the mess she had fallen into.

But she was to be pleasantly surprised by something Bridie had to say when, having been over to the paddock to see that the seven donkeys were being fed and watered by Kimon, she went to see the Irish girl, whose visitors had gone to the island of Cos for a couple of days.

'Guess what?' said Bridie with her customary vivaciousness. 'Denis and Helena, the sister of one of our maids were at the village dance the night before last, and he saw her again last evening. According to our maid—Lefki, I don't think you've met her yet—Denis is very much taken with Helena!'

'It's rather sudden, isn't it?' Kim recalled her meeting with Denis on the morning after the scene in the garden, Denis had been sullen, denouncing her husband as an arrogant snob who was far too aware of his own importance.

In spite of Vidas's decision not to retain his services, Kim had pleaded with Denis to stay. The whole thing would blow over, she assured him. He felt guilty, she realised, and played on this a little, saying that the situation would never have arisen had it not been for his impulsive action in kissing her. Denis finally agreed to stay, having first reminded Kim that her husband could not dismiss him on the spot without paying him a month's salary. Kim was optimistic enough to hope that Bridie's husband could now be persuaded to pay something towards Denis's salary. In addition, Denis was, in fact, intending to attempt to being a private practise, as he had already been asked to do by one or two of the more affluent smallholders on the island. He was at that very time going over to help a farmer whose cow was having difficulty calving. Denis said finally, 'I realise my folly in thinking there could be anything between you and me, Kim. Forgive me for the trouble I've caused.'

'Perhaps it is sudden,' agreed Bridie, recalling Kim from her musings, but went on to say that she hoped something would come of it, first because Helena was such a charming girl, and second because it would put an end to any complications that might have set in. Kim of course knew to what she referred and naturally made no comment. But if it should transpire that Denis became serious about Helena, Vidas would have nothing to complain about; he could no longer adopt the attitude he had at present adopted. Kim's spirits were light as she made her way home. She would seek out Vidas immediately and relate what Bridie had told her. But as soon as she entered the grounds she saw Floria, wandering along a flower-bordered path edging the wide front lawn. A sudden wave of anger swept over Kim, and involuntarily, she quickened her pace.

Floria stopped and waited, her cool, alert stare travelling the length of Kim's figure, taking in the crisp cotton dress with its blue and red flowers on a cream background, the dainty blue sandals and matching bag slung over her shoulder. Kim's hair was windswept for she had come part of the way along the beach; her skin had a healthy honey glow and her lips were rosy red. In her eyes there was a gleam of enquiry, but Floria did not speak. She left Kim to break the silence.

'I'm surprised to see you here,' said Kim. 'I thought you'd gone back to Rhodes.'

'I've been home and come back again. I lost a very valuable diamond and sapphire bracelet somewhere and had to come and see if I could find it.'

Kim eyed her suspiciously, half doubting her word, then chiding herself for her mistrust. What would it benefit Floria to come back if she had no reason for doing so? 'Vidas knows you are here?'

'No, I arrived an hour ago to find he was out. I've been searching for my bracelet but haven't had any luck. I've left Adela looking for it.'

'You don't know where you lost it?'

'I have no idea.'

'Then why aren't you at Bridie's?'

'I might stay there tonight, but I came straight here because I'm sure I lost the bracelet that night I dined—'

She broke off and her crimson mouth curved in what Kim put down as an amused sneer. 'The night Vidas found you in your lover's arms.' Slowly the girl swung round and reached out to snap off a delicate spray of magenta bougainvillaea, which she began to twirl in her long, red-tipped fingers while Kim could only stare, dumbfounded, at the girl's outspokenness. 'I don't blame you for taking a lover. It's the fashionable thing to do in Greece and—'

'Don't you feel you would be better occupied in looking for your bracelet?' cut in Kim, managing to speak at last. 'It seems very strange that you are out here, wasting your time, when you could be putting it to more profitable use.'

Floria's lovely mouth went tight. 'Don't adopt that high-handed manner with me,' she snapped. 'Unless I'm very much mistaken, you won't be here much longer. Vidas will divorce you because he's not the man to tolerate infidelity in his wife, no matter what the reason he had for marrying her . . .' A significant pause followed as Floria stared insolently at Kim, a sneer curing her mouth. 'Everyone knows why he had to get married. His stepmother was driving him to distraction. He must now realise he made a mistake and should have married me last year, when we were . . . lovers.'

'Lovers?' Even though Kim was not really surprised, the actual knowledge brought torment to her mind.

'Of course we were lovers.'

'And you don't mind admitting it?'

'I've just said, it's the fashionable thing to do in Greece.'

Kim looked at her with deep contempt, still staggered by the lack of restraint in her speech. At length she said, 'If Vidas had wanted to marry you last year, then he would have done so.'

Strangely, Floria made no comment on this. She seemed fully absorbed in dismantling the spray she still held in her hand, carelessly stripping away each delicate petal and tossing it into the air to be carried on the breeze, like a miniature kite. Several floated to an ornamental pool, where they were transformed into tiny yachts, sails gleaming in the sunshine.

Kim watched her with the sort of fascination, wondering how anyone could deliberately destroy anything as beautiful as the spray of bougainvillaea. At last she walked away, her head high and her steps brisk, but her heart was dragging within her, for the girl's words about divorce had found a target, and Kim could not put them out of her mind. Did Vidas really believe his wife guilty of infidelity? Had what he'd seen in the garden recalled all his initial beliefs, all his old contempt for her? He had originally branded her a no-good, then been forced to change his opinion about her character. And now, as she dwelt on her earlier suspicion that he was fighting against the possibility of falling in love with her, she had to admit that the reason for this could only be that even before that scene in the garden when he had caught her in Denis's arms, he had still held on to some of those initial beliefs. She recalled his saying that she had wanted to marry his brother for his money, and she had told him this was not true, that she never had any intention of marrying his brother, and had at the time been confident that Vidas had believed her. But now she realised she could have been wrong and that although he had listened attentively to her denial, he had not accepted it as the truth. This would account for his reluctance to become emotionally involved with her. He still believed she was not worthy of him.

Slowly she made her way through the hall towards the ornate balustraded stairway, then to her surprise Vidas emerged from his study. 'I was told you were out,' she said, recovering from her surprise.

'I was; I've been in about five minutes.' He searched her face with a cold stare. 'Did you want to see me about something?'

'You didn't come in the front way?' she said, and saw a frown of puzzlement appear on his forehead.

'I came in by the moat entrance. Why do you ask?'

She hesitated a moment and then, 'Floria's looking for you. She's in the garden.' With a toss of her head Kim would have left him, but his hand shot out and she was brought roughly around to face him again.

'Floria? What does she want?' He gave Kim no time to answer as he added, 'There's something wrong. What is it?'

Kim tugged at her hand, then winced as her husband's grip tightened about her wrist. His face was dark, forbidding, his whole manner overbearing and arrogant.

'Floria's been talking to me about certain things . . .' Kim's eyes filled up but she lowered her lashes so that he could not see. 'All I will say to you, Vidas, is that your judgment of what happened out there in the garden the other night was way out of line. You jumped to conclusions that were all wrong. However, it's really of no importance, is it, not at this stage in our relationship?' She gave another tug and this time took him by surprise. She stared down at the faint bruise on her wrist and her lip quivered. Then she turned away, aware of his strange expression and the stillness around her. She said over her shoulder, 'One other thing, Vidas, I'm not willing to be your wife; from now on our relationship reverts to what it was in the beginning. Just get that straight and keep to your own bedroom!'

'Kim!' he called imperiously, but she was running up the stairs. He did not come after her, and when she looked through her window, she saw him striding out across the lawn towards a little woodland glade of immense trees into which Floria was just disappearing.

Chapter Eleven

Bridie stared at her friend in stunned disbelief, words failing her. Kim, biting her lip in vexation, wondered what had possessed her to confide so much to the girl she would never see again after she left the island. For leave she must, and in the near future; she could not continue to live with Vidas much longer. After she had spoken to him outside his study, then seen him striding purposefully across the lawn after Floria, Kim had cherished the hope that he would come to her room later and put everything right in her mind. But it hadn't turned out like that at all. On the contrary, Vidas had acted as if nothing had happened—except that he had respected her wish for him to keep to his own bedroom. That had been two days ago and Kim's nerves had suffered acutely. She lacked all ability to concentrate and had no interest in her project. She had talked with Bridie and Denis about it, true, but both must have noticed her waning interest in what at first had fired her with such enthusiasm that she had been able to pass it on to several other people.

At last Bridie spoke, her customery vivaciousness lost beneath the sadness in her tone. 'I must admit that George was convinced Vidas had married you in order to get rid of Alexandra, but I refused to listen—at least, after I'd met you. But I still cannot associate divorce with a man like your husband. Besides, Floria did not say that Vidas actually mentioned divorce.'

'I'm sure he's thinking about it, Bridie. You see, he believes there was something between Denis and me—and you can't blame him, can you?'

'Surely you have explained it all to Vidas?'

'What is there to explain? Denis was kissing me and I was making no attempt to stop him. Another few seconds and yes, I would certainly have done something, but those seconds were not granted to me. Vidas just happened to come upon the scene.' Kim's eyes were shadowed with regret. It was another act of fate, and this time fate had denied her that fleeting moment which would have made such a difference in her life and in her relationship with her husband. They had become friends, intimate companions and lovers, and her hopes of winning his love had soared. Then, stupidly, she had decided to make Vidas jealous, with disastrous results.

'I feel sure Vidas hasn't any intention of divorcing you, Kim, in spite of what he saw.'

Bridie's words recalled her and Kim said unhappily, 'I'd far rather a divorce than that he have Floria as his pillow-friend.'

'What seems so inexplicable to me,' said Bridie, 'is that he hasn't referred to Floria and what transpired between them. You must agree it's very strange indeed?'

'If what she said is true, it could be that he's ashamed of himself. I can imagine his not wanting to admit that he made a mistake in not marrying her.'

'Well, he didn't marry her, and that left him free for another year. Yes, he had a full year to make up his mind if he wanted her or not. Then you came along, meeting him in the most unusual circumstances. But you and he agreed to marry, for your mutual advantage. In my opinion he's honour-bound to remain married to you—and faithful!'

A wry smile touched the outline of Kim's mouth. 'By your own admission Greek men are unfaithful.'

'Not all,' was Bridie's swift and emphatic denial. 'My George is faithful, and I know of others who are. I always imagined that when Vidas married he would be too.'

'If he'd married for love, he probably would have been,' Kim said, and a deep sigh escaped her friend.

'What a mess! And what a pity Denis was stupid enough to kiss you!'

'Bridie,' said Kim, as she recalled again what Floria had said, 'if Vidas had already regretted marrying me instead of Floria, then he'd have asked for a divorce anyway. The scene in the garden has only hastened matters.'

'Why did Floria have to see it!'

'Vidas said she would spread it all over the island.'

'He did?' with a new and inexplicable interest. 'Kim, does it not strike you as strange that a man would make that kind of subtle accusation about the woman he wants to marry?'

Kim's lashes fluttered. She said slowly, 'I'd not given it a thought. In fact, it's only now that I've remembered it.'

'He must have been mad at her at the time.'

'I don't think he was mad, just distrustful.'

Bridie's brows lifted a fraction. 'Isn't that as bad?'

Kim looked at her. 'What are you trying to say, Bridie?'

'I'm saying that there's something about this whole thing that's not at all clear. Why don't you ask Vidas outright if he intends to ask for a divorce?'

'It isn't for me to broach the subject. He knows that Floria was talking to me, and if he had been puzzled about anything, then he would have straightened it all out then.'

'But Floria went home that same evening. Don't you see, Kim, that if there was anything between them, he'd have asked her to stay? Last year, when they were so close, she was here, with us, for weeks on end, but this time she didn't even stay one night—although she told you she might stay with us. What made her leave the island so quickly?'

Kim became thoughtful, deliberating on her friend's words. Always she came back to the one thing: if Vidas had anything to say that was different from what Floria had said, then he would have approached his wife and all would have been explained.

'I can't be in any way optimistic,' she confessed at last. 'By his very silence Vidas is convincing me that what Floria said was the truth, and that he regrets not having married her.'

Later that day, Kim decided to walk down to a small café on the waterfront. As she strolled along her heart was so heavy that she felt she must tell Vidas that very evening that she was leaving his home. Where would she go, though? With her parents' home sold and her own job gone, she felt lost and helpless, a wanderer, alone with no base, a ship without an anchor. How did one begin to build an entirely new life when the old one had been shattered, everything broken and lost, irrecoverable? If only she had relatives—other than her parents, for she had no intention of going to them—sisters preferably, who would be there to rely on, to help constructively.

Kim made her way to the charming little outdoor *cafeneion* where the tables with their snowy white cloths were placed in a garden hedged in on three sides by flaring hibiscus bushes, where shade was provided by the vines woven through overhead trellises, the huge green bunches of grapes there for all customers to help themselves. All you had to do was reach up and take your pick of the lush ripe fruit.

There was the usual mixture of customers—a couple of tourists, Americans on a tour of Europe, and a seaman with a black roll-neck jersey sitting with his wife, who was nursing a baby. Several men were playing *tavli* while a few others stood by the tables and watched, cigarettes dangling from thick sensual lips, worry beads twirling automatically. Why was it that in these Eastern countries it was always assumed that the men had all the worries?

Kim sat down at a table close to the American couple. She gave her order and the woman said, 'You're English, aren't you? We've just come from London. Gee, but we loved every minute of our stay there!'

'Where else did you go?' asked Kim, wondering how so many Americans could afford to be travelling half their lives.

'France and Spain—'

'I mean in England.'

'Oh, we just stayed around London. There is so much to see!'

'And time went so quickly,' interposed her husband.

'London,' said Kim wistfully, 'is not England.'

'Well, we know that, but—'

'Just as New York is not America. If I ever go to your country, I want to see far more than one big, bustling city. I want to see the beauty that man has not messed up.' Why was she talking like this to strangers? she wondered. It must be the mood she was in that made her feel resentful that they had not made the effort to see a little more of her beautiful country.

'Whereabouts do you live?' the woman asked with interest. 'You see, we intend to come again next year, and we're going to take note of what you say. We'd like to come and see you, wouldn't we, Randy?'

'Very much . . .' He was feeling in his pocket as he spoke, and he brought forth a wallet. Extracting a card, he handed it to her. 'That's where we live, in Oregon. Our home is right on the Pacific Ocean, and we have a lovely breeze all the time. You're welcome to stay with us if ever you come over that way.'

'Thank you.' Kim took the card and, after looking at it, slipped it into her handbag.

'Where do you live?' asked the woman again.

'At present I am living here, on the island.'

'Here? But how wonderful! You've been here some time?'

'Perhaps, Jan,' interrupted Randy, 'the young lady doesn't want to answer all these questions.'

'Oh, it doesn't matter,' said Kim swiftly. 'I've been here since my marriage.'

'You're married to one of these handsome Greeks?'

Kim had to smile as she glanced around at the assortment of stocky, swarthy men sitting about in the café.

'I am married to a Greek yes . . .' Her voice faded and a hint of colour touched her cheeks. 'Here is my husband,' she murmured from the depths of a dry, parched throat. 'He—he doesn't usually come into town. . . .' He had seen her and soon he was standing by her table. Kim frowned, wondering how he came to be here.

He said stiffly, 'May I join you, Kim?'

'Of c-course,' she stammered, and then, in an effort to regain her composure, she introduced him to the couple she had been speaking to. Within seconds they had moved over to her table, Vidas having picked up Jan's chair when he realised what was happening.

'Thank you very much.' Jan smiled up at him, her blue eyes laughing and appreciative. 'I knew that this young lady would have a tall handsome husband,' she said. 'We've just been making friends with one another, but we haven't yet discovered her name.'

'It's Kim,' supplied Vidas, his strong white teeth flashing in a smile, 'and mine's Vidas.' His dark eyes slid to his wife's face with a look of sardonic amusement, because of the surprise she evinced at his spontaneous friendliness to strangers. Her colour fluctuated and she lowered her lashes. Vidas clapped his hands imperiously and a waiter came at once.

Vidas glanced around the table and asked if he could order anything for the American couple. Randy said he would have a beer and Jan had another lemonade with ice. Kim said she had already ordered.

'And *ouzo* for me,' said Vidas, then turned to Randy to ask how long they would be on the island.

'We're here for another two days. We originally came for a weekend but we love the beaches, and so we decided to stay a little longer.'

'Where are you staying?'

'The Aphrodite Hotel on Livia Bay.'

'The best hotel on the island.'

'We're very satisfied with it.' The waiter came with the tray, and after the pause in conversation Jan said, 'How about you two joining us for dinner this evening? We'd love to have company; we usually dine at about eight o'clock but we could meet for drinks first.' She was eager, vivacious, reminding Kim of Bridie, but Jan was older, around forty-five, she estimated.

Kim looked at Vidas, fully expecting him to decline the offer and to resist any further persuasion with that sort of courteous immovability she herself had encountered on more than one occasion. But much to her surprise he readily accepted, without consulting her.

'Then that's settled!' Jan was delighted and Randy was equally happy. 'It's so nice to make friends on one's travels, isn't it?'

Kim said curiously, 'Have you been travelling for a long time—on this present trip, I mean?'

The two looked at one another in an intimate kind of way before Jan said, 'It's our honeymoon. Randy insisted on a prolonged one, so we've been away from home for almost a year. We had less than a month in our lovely new house before he swept me away, but now I'm more than ready to go back.'

'A whole year,' breathed Kim, shaking her head. 'I can understand your wanting to get back to your house. After all, there's no place on earth like your own particular home. . . .' Her voice trailed into silence as she noticed her husband's eyes fixed upon her. It was almost as if he read her mind, knew she was contemplating leaving him and the home that had been hers for so short a time.

Conversation continued for another half hour or so before they rose from the table and said good-bye.

'Only for the present,' smiled Randy. 'We'll look forward to seeing you at about seven-thirty.'

Alone with Vidas, Kim said quietly, 'I took it for granted that you would refuse their offer.'

'That's not surprising,' he returned dryly. 'You take so many things for granted.'

The subtle meaning escaped her and she asked what he was talking about.

'It doesn't matter,' he said casually. They began to walk slowly along the waterfront, passing fishermen mending nets and others selling their catch. One grizzled old man carrying the stamp of a lifetime at sea was squatting on the pavement slapping an octopus on the concrete, creating the frothy white substance that would tenderise the fish. 'How did you come to be here?' Vidas enquired, slanting Kim a glance.

'I felt like a walk,' was all she said, then asked him why he had been in town.

'Like you, I felt like walking,' was his unexpected rejoinder. 'And like you I decided to have some refreshment in Stamati's *cafeneion*.'

'Are you walking back or shall we call a taxi?'

'Which do you prefer?'

'I'm agreeable either way.' They were talking for the sake of it, she thought, a deep sadness enveloping her at the lack of cordiality in their manner of speech. Yes, it would be best if they parted—and the sooner the better.

Kim was undecided as to what to wear for dinner at the hotel. Since coming to Malindos she had been used to wearing an ankle-length dress, but knowing that dining out was often an informal affair these days, she decided it would be wise to ask her husband's advice. He spoke quietly when, after tapping on his bedroom door, she called his name.

'What is it?' Opening the door, he stood there, looking down at her with an interrogative expression on his face.

'Shall I wear a long dress?' Her tone was equally soft, her eyes lowered so that he could not read her expression.

'Haven't you a mid-length evening dress?'

'Of course.'

'Then wear that.' He stood a moment, in an attitude oddly suggestive of indecision, as if there were something he would like to say to her. For some reason she turned away, a pain at her heart as the door closed behind her. Instinctively, she knew the moment had been lost.

She glanced in the long gilt-framed mirrow when she was ready, the perfume spray in her hand. She wore a cocktail dress of larkspur-blue, the waist nipped in below a tight-fitting strapless bodice. The skirt, full and flowing, was trimmed round the hem with deep blue lace, which was matched by the trimming round the top of the bodice. Kim used the perfume, drew a comb through her gleaming hair again, and then, aware that Vidas was still moving about in his room, she waited, her eyes wandering to the window and the glowing outline of flaming treetops in the garden. She moved, opened the window, and stepped through onto the balustraded stone balcony. Her brooding eyes stared into the distance where, in another direction, the sea joined the sky in the silver haze of oncoming dusk. She watched the sun go down swiftly, watched the dusk fall softly, covering the landscape. The eddy of a breeze carried the tang of the sea and the added perfumes it had gathered on the way. Twilight in the East was short, and even as she stood there shadows closed in around her, mysterious and cool. Suddenly she shivered; Vidas was behind her, and she felt his hand on her arms as he turned her round to face him. Acutely aware of the stress in their relationship, she felt the tears film her eyes, but he couldn't see and she was glad.

'What are you thinking, out here so quiet and alone?'

'Fate brought me here,' she said, which was not an answer but the thought that had come unbidden into her mind.

'Fate rules our lives.'

'It can be malignant at times,' she said, and felt him give a start.

'That's a strong word, Kim.'

'Fate brought Dendras and I together; fate killed him. It was fate that made my parents adopt Stephen and suffer for their kindness. Fate's malignant,' she repeated.

He said nothing and she would have loved to see his

face clearly. But it was in full shadow, and freeing herself, she turned again to stare broodingly down into the gardens where a shower of creamy moonglow had already vanquished the mothy darkness; it shone through the branches of the twisted olive trees; it adorned the cascading waters of the fountain with a thousand scintillating diamonds. A night for romance . . . Again Kim's mind was filled with thoughts of the stress in their relationship.

'I suppose we ought to be moving.' Her voice was still and cool. 'What time is it?'

'A quarter past seven. You are right; we ought to be on our way.'

He drove the car in silence. Kim was conscious of a nerve-twisting tension within her and made an effort to relax. It was difficult, for she suddenly had the sensation of being poised on the edge of a cliff . . . and of wanting to jump. They stormy torrent of Vidas's fury was preferable to this stolid silence he was adopting. She wondered if he wanted to tell her of his decision to end the marriage but was having difficulty in finding an approach. Well, she would save him the trouble. Tonight she would tell him that as far as she was concerned, the marriage was ended and she would be leaving the castle almost immediately. This resolve, though it relieved some of the tension, brought back with stark reality the fact that she had nowhere to go when she landed in England. However, she did have a little money, despite what she had been spending on her project, and this would see her through the first couple of months. She sighed as she tried to visualise what would happen to the donkeys she had rescued, and decided to ask this one favour of Vidas, that he would leave them where they were and have them cared for by the gardeners, as was being done at present. Kim felt sure that Bridie and Denis would carry on, especially as two more volunteers had come forward in the past week. No one was indispensable and they could do very well without her.

Jan and Randy were in the hotel lobby waiting for them, and greetings followed their entrance before they all retired to the lounge, where they chatted over predinner drinks. It was during this time that they exchanged surnames and Kim learned that Randy was of Irish extraction, as were so many Americans. His name was Kelly.

'You'd be interested to meet my friend Bridie,' Kim said conversationally. 'She's from Galway.'

'Galway!' exclaimed Jan. 'That's where Randy's people came from!'

'Perhaps you would like me to arrange a meeting with Bridie, then?'

'Oh, would you, Kim? That would be great! Is she married?'

'Yes, to a Greek.'

'She is? Then ask them to dine with us tomorrow evening—here at the hotel.'

'How about you all coming to dine with Kim and me tomorrow?' interjected Vidas, ignoring the start of surprise his wife could not suppress.

'That would be wonderful,' said Randy. 'Do you live on this side of the island?'

'No, the other side.' Vidas had a calling card in his breast pocket. Before he handed it to Randy, he explained how to get to the castle. Randy took the card, and Kim had to smile at his widening gaze and the slow, almost reluctant way he passed the card into his wife's impatient hand.

173

'A castle! We've seen the ruins of a few Venetian castles, down in the valley, and we saw two that have been restored.'·

'The one on the cliff is where Bridie lives,' Kim informed them.

'So Bridie lives in a castle too?'

'That's right.'

'And you live in the other? It seemed to us that it had fantastic views.'

'You will see for yourself tomorrow,' said Vidas in a casual tone, as he accepted a menu from the waiter who had appeared at their table.

The evening went off splendidly, and it seemed to Kim that Vidas could not possibly be contemplating divorce. Both Randy and Jan passed remarks as to how happy she and her husband were, and it was Vidas who vouchsafed the information that they had been married only a few months.

'So we're all on our honeymoons!' exclaimed Jan, who had earlier confided to Kim that it was the second time round for both Randy and herself. She said little about her first husband, but it was not difficult for Kim to guess that the marriage had been a bad experience almost from the start. Randy's case was different; he had been happily married until the death of his wife eight years ago. He was now fifty-two and his three children—two boys and a girl—were all married. So he had considered himself free to marry again if he wished. It so happened that he and Jan had actually met at the wedding of his son Jeremy, who was the last of the three to marry and leave home. On deciding to marry, Jan and Randy sold their homes and bought the one in Oregon. 'We decided that memories would be gathered by us, for us,' she said, and Kim thought what a wonderful philosophy that was. 'Memories gathered by us, for us . . .' Kim wished that Vidas had heard. But would it have made any difference? Looking at him, noting the softened lines of his face as he chatted to Randy, Kim asked herself if it was really Floria he wanted to marry . . . Floria, who would give him an heir, and perhaps other children.

It was not long after that silent question that Kim, with a little throb of uneasiness, attempted to push something from her mind, which she knew had been hovering in its far recesses for about a week. The morning after the dinner with the Kellys, as soon as she rose from her bed, she felt nausea spread through her body. A quivering hand went automatically to her stomach.

It had been after midnight when she and Vidas arrived back, after sitting for more than two hours in the hotel lounge, chatting with their newfound friends over coffee and liqueurs. Kim had quite naturally abandoned the idea of speaking to Vidas about a separation; it could keep till the morning, she decided . . . but now . . .

Strangely, the leap of perception came with a suddenness she would never have expected, and weak from a sense of shock, she sank down on the bed, dragging her damp palms over the coverlet.

'It isn't true!' she cried. 'No, I won't accept it!' Yet even while one part of her mind uttered the denial, she admitted at last what an inner voice had been persistently claiming, though she had refused to listen. Or perhaps she had not wanted to hear. It was impossible now to thrust away what she had known for some days. She was expecting her husband's child. . . .

What must she do? If she told him of her condition, he would naturally give up all thoughts of a divorce. But would he give up all thoughts of Floria? Kim rather thought they would take up where they had left off; they would become pillow-friends again. That sort of life was not for her, decided Kim, resolving there and then to keep to her original intention of telling him she was leaving. He wanted a divorce, and therefore he would have to give her a settlement. That would suffice for her child and herself. Vidas would never even know she had had his child.

Tears gathered in her eyes as desolation swept over her. She loved her husband with a devotion that bordered on the spiritual, and yet she was forced to leave him, never to see him again as long as she lived. And when he was married and another child came along—Floria's son—he would be the heir. . . .

It seemed, for a fleeting moment, that Kim's heart stopped beating. For something had affected her as she thought of her child being robbed of his rightful heritage. It was something she could never allow to happen, and this meant she had to make a decision; either she would stay and suffer any pain inflicted by her husband's infidelity, or she would resign herself to giving up her child at a later date, when he was older and no longer needed a mother's love, so he could claim his rightful inheritance.

Chapter Twelve

It was natural that making such a crucial decision should take time, and after hours of conflicting resolutions, followed by a feeling of helplessness, Kim tried to give her mind a rest. She had reached the state where a decision was impossible anyway.

She went out to the garden, where she had always found peace walking among the flowers, delighting in the plumage of the birds, marvelling at their song. If she did decide to leave, these walks would be remembered always . . . 'memories gathered by me, for me,' she whispered against the lump in her throat. It was not to be as it was with Randy and Jan . . . 'memories gathered by us, for us.'

Kim went over to the waste ground where the paddocks were. She kept a stock of carrots and sugar lumps in a box close by, and as soon as she approached, all seven donkeys came ambling towards her, three in one paddock and four in another. After feeding them with the tidbits she decided to go down to the harbour where, at one end, the animal dispensary was being built. The main structural work was finished and now work was going on inside. The whole project had aroused a great deal of interest, and as she approached she had to smile at the men standing there, some in *vraga*—baggy black pantaloons—chewing on tobacco while flicking and twirling the inevitable worry beads. They stared, a wide-eyed expression coming to their faces only when Kim approached. They moved aside, first having examined her from head to toe, stripping her. She was used to it; every Greek male subjected every female to the same scrutiny, be the man old or young, married or single.

'*Yassoo*, Kim!' cried Bridie who came to the door just as Kim arrived.

'*Yassoo!*' returned Kim, noticing the amusement of the men at the girls' use of the Greek greeting. It was almost always used in the afternoon, but it did not mean good afternoon, Kim had soon learned. Its meaning was more like, 'Hail to you!'

'Hello, Kim.' Denis came to the door to stand beside Bridie. 'Come on in and see what we're doing.' He was smiling and looked happy. Kim glanced at Bridie, and as soon as she was able to snatch a moment alone with her she asked how Denis's affair with Helena was progressing.

'By leaps and bounds. In fact, I'm going to ask him outright if it's serious.'

'You are?'

'Why not? Bridie shrugged. 'If he is serious, it'll be common knowledge soon anyway. You can't keep secrets in a place like this.'

Denis was talking to one of the workmen, a joiner who was making a set of cupboards and some wall cabinets. When eventually Denis came back to them, Bridie said blandly, 'When is the engagement to be announced?'

He was startled at first, then amused. 'Bridie, you're the limit!'

'So George is always telling me. Well?'

'We're very happy together.' He seemed a trifle embarrassed as he met Kim's gaze, but he soon recovered his composure and added musingly, 'I suppose there isn't much for us to wait for, not really. Helena doesn't seem to mind being poor.'

'You have a lovely villa, Denis. Any girl would like to live there.'

'Yes, but it's only rented. Helena has a dowry house, as her brother tentatively mentioned yesterday—'

'Eager to get one of his sisters married, eh? You know why, don't you? He wants to get married himself but can't until both his sisters are off their parents' hands.'

Kim was looking puzzled, and it was Denis who explained that in the villages of Greece, and on many of the small islands, the dowry system still prevailed, and this also carried the obligation of brothers to work to help provide a dowry house for each sister. Andreas and his father had built Helena's over a period of five years, using all they earned and all their time. Cousins and other relatives had helped, and the resulting villa was very pretty, set in a lemon orchard not far from where Helena and her brother lived. Maroula, the other sister, was at present living at Bridie's home but she too must be provided with a house before she could hope to marry.

'I told him that if I married Helena I wouldn't hear of accepting a dowry,' said Denis, whereupon Bridie declared that Andreas would be delighted, because Helena's house could then go to Maroula, which meant she would soon find a husband. That would leave Andreas free to marry his Souphoula, who was already twenty-seven and had been waiting for him since she was nineteen.

'You are thinking of marrying Helena, then?' persisted Bridie, and after a slight pause Denis nodded and said yes, he was very seriously thinking of marrying Helena.

'So we're all going to be invited to the engagement ceremony?'

'I expect so.'

Kim had already learned that an engagement was solemnised by a church ceremony and was as binding as the marriage. The prospective bride and groom dressed up and so did the guests. The couple would exchange gold rings, which they would wear on their right hands until, at the actual wedding, they would be switched to the left.

'Well, let us all know.' Bridie grinned at him. 'I'll bet you never thought you'd find a wife almost as soon as you arrived here.'

'Indeed no.' Denis's expression was rueful. 'Nor did I expect to be able to build up a practise.'

Kim's eyes went to his. 'You've managed to get more clients, then?'

Denis nodded his head. 'I was approached yesterday by a hotel owner who's buying two Labradors from Rhodes. He wants me to look after them—give them a six-monthly medical and the necessary injections.'

'That's great!' from Bridie. 'And promising. People will tell one another.'

'I'm not expecting much, Bridie, but every little bit is going to help.' His eyes slid fleetingly to Kim. She looked away, but just before she left, she managed to get him alone for a moment.

'You'll get your salary, Denis,' she assured him. 'When Vidas knows you are engaged to Helena, then he'll forget what happened that night.'

'I don't care whether he does or not; I have some money saved, and as I've said, there's a chance of my building up a small practise. Helena and I can manage.'

Kim left shortly afterwards, with Bridie, who had her car.

'I'll drop you off,' she said, and although Kim would have preferred to walk, she accepted the lift. 'See you soon,' said Bridie, as she prepared to drive away from the castle. 'I'll give you a ring in the morning.'

Kim watched the car disappear and an added weight dragged at her spirits at the thought of losing the friend she had so recently made.

It was later in the day that Kim found her footsteps guided toward the little Byzantine church in which she had been married—the Church of San Demetrius with its honey-coloured walls, its impressive dome and red tiled roof. It stood to one side of the Halthea Valley, high above the vineyards and citrus orchards Vidas owned. The view from the rise was breathtaking, over the ochre-pink hills to one side, out to the indigo sea on another, while to the east rose the serrated mountains, pewter-dark and ominous against the brittle Grecian sky. Nestling on a plateau, the little village of Saldenos could be seen, remnant of the fine city that had been the island's centre of culture when the Venetians had been rulers of Malindos and several other islands close by. What a chequered history Greece had, Kim mused as she went into the church, stopping to admire the lovely mosaics and the simple dignity of the white marble statues. As her nostrils caught the pungent smell of incense she was poignantly reminded of her wedding day, the ceremony that had joined her to a man she had come to love, but who would never love her.

The silence within the church was absolute as she lingered there, facing the altar. How long she had been standing there before the sound reached her ears she did not know, but it was so slight that she did not even turn her head, believing it to be the mere whisper of a breeze drifting in from the warm bright hills.

'Kim . . .' Her name came softly and she stiffened, feeling guilty, like a child caught trespassing.

Over her shoulder she said quietly, 'What do you want, Vidas?'

'Why have you come here?' He was beside her, and as always she felt the power of him, the magnetism that had drawn her from the very first meeting between them.

'I don't quite know,' she answered. 'My footsteps just led me and I—I was here.' It was not the answer she would have given him had she stopped to think, but she just said what was in her mind, probably because it was the truth.

She heard her husband say, 'I saw you climbing the hill. You looked tired.' He sounded anxious, she thought, and turned her head a little to examine his expression. She saw only the familiar stern features, and the wild pulsation of a nerve in his cheek.

'I'm not tired.' No, it was not tiredness that had caused her feet to drag; it was the heaviness within her. 'Why did you come?' she asked.

'To see why you were here.' He came round to face her, towering above her as always. Kim's eyes were soft and smoky as she lifted her face to meet his gaze. 'You're pale,' he observed. Kim said nothing, and in the pause that followed she had the impression that he was seeking words. They came at last. 'I have something to say to you—'.

'Not here, Vidas.' Kim's voice was low but firm. 'It isn't the place.'

'Not the place.' He looked at her with a puzzled expression. 'What do you mean?'

'We were married here; it isn't the place to begin discussions about a divorce. Besides, I haven't yet made up my mind. What I mean is, I had intended to provide an easy solution to your problem; I was willing to talk to you about a separation but something's happened. . . .' Her voice trailed off as she began to pull herself up. She had made her decision! It had come swiftly after all the painful indecision of the morning. She would *not* agree to a separation. She would suffer if she had to, but better that than her child deprived of the luxury of his rightful home. 'We will talk if you want, but not here.' She turned to go, her eyes staring past him to the scene framed in the church doorway— the ancient gravestones, mellowed and sadly atilt, the line of yew trees darkly oppressive, and through a gap, the sun-bright hills outlined against the sky.

'Just a minute.' Vidas barred her way. 'Where did you get all this about a divorce?'

'Floria—but you will never get me out of the castle. I'm here to stay.'

'I never intended it to be otherwise.'

'Not at first, perhaps, but Floria convinced me that you want her. Well, you can have her, Vidas, but it'll be as a mistress, not as a wife.' Anger was rising but she meant to control it—at least while she was in church. 'You knew that Floria had been talking to me that day in the garden—it was the day she came back to find her lost bracelet. You went out to speak to her and . . . and I thought you might have come back to me to—to explain, to say that what Floria said was all wrong. But you didn't come back and you've never mentioned it since, so it's plain that she *was* right, isn't it?' She looked at him, her eyes big in her face.

'You didn't tell me what she said to you.' Vidas's voice was taut; Kim had the impression that he too was battling with his temper.

'She said you regretted not marrying her last year when—when you were lovers. She convinced me you wanted a divorce.'

'She told you we were lovers?' He gritted his teeth, ignoring the rest.

'She said it was fashionable in Greece.' Kim pulled herself up and, frowning, tried again to leave the church. 'I'm not talking about such things here,' she almost snapped. 'Please let me pass.'

'Not until I have had my say.' He put out his hands to rest them on her shoulders, felt her quiver beneath his touch, and for a second he closed his eyes, as if pained by something he now bitterly regretted. 'I've been a fool, Kim, in trying to fight something that had me beaten weeks ago.' Before she had time to marshal her thoughts and find something to say, his mouth closed on hers, and for a long time he held her to his heart.

Was it true? she asked herself. Had the miracle she had once prayed for really happened?

'Oh, Vidas, is it true?' Kim gasped out the question when at last he released her. 'You—you love me?'

'Forever,' was his fervent reply and he bent to kiss her again before continuing to explain. 'As you know, dearest, I was determined never to become emotionally involved with a woman. From what I had seen, it was always obvious to me that love does not last, and so I never intended to weaken—' He broke off there and gave a tender, rueful laugh, looking deeply into her eyes and shaking his head. 'I hadn't a chance, though, not once I'd learned that you'd never been Dendras's pillow-friend. But still I fought on, like a fool, making us both unhappy. Yes, darling,' he said in answer to her glance of surprise, 'I knew you loved me. When I was away in Athens I missed you so much that I had to admit I loved you, but my pride had been injured by the easy way you managed to deceive me right at the start, and every time I wanted to be tender with you, my thoughts would invariably stray to that and the result was an immediate return of my animosity. And in my stubborn foolishness I swore I'd never forgive you.'

'I suspected you were fighting your love for me, Vidas, and so I tried to—to entice you.' The bald admission earned her a little shake as punishment, but the next moment Vidas was kissing her tenderly, his warm hands gentle as they held her close. 'I then had the idea of making you jealous,' continued Kim, when he drew his lips from hers. 'So I suggested—'

'Inviting Denis over for dinner,' he finished for her. 'It was because I suspected you of that sort of wile that

I retaliated by inviting Floria. It was only meant as a joke, but when I came outside with her and found you in Denis's arms—'

'But if you knew I loved you, then you also knew there was nothing between Denis and me, so I don't understand your anger.'

'No? With Floria looking on and the sure conviction that she'd spread it all over the island?'

'I don't think she did talk, Vidas.'

'We shall never know, nor do I care, not now.'

'Did she find her bracelet—?' Kim broke off, aware that the question was unimportant.

'She never lost one.'

Kim was not too surprised by this piece of information. 'What happened when you went out to her?' she asked curiously, after a pause.

'She admitted she'd come back specifically to find out whether or not there was a rift between you and me as a result of what I saw out there in the garden. I said no and sent her packing.'

'Sent her packing?' repeated Kim.

'Told her to clear off. I was married and so our affair was ended.'

'It wasn't fair to invite her to dinner,' chided Kim. 'It gave her ideas.' Although Vidas nodded in rapid agreement, he made no comment. It was plain that he had no wish to waste time talking about his old flame. 'Why didn't you come back to me and explain?'

'Because I was still mad at seeing my wife in another man's arms. You didn't appear to be putting up much of a fight, either!'

'I can explain,' offered Kim hurriedly, and she did, ending up by telling Vidas about the upcoming engage-

186

ment between Denis and Helena and asking that Denis be reinstated in his job.

'Yes, he can have his job back,' said Vidas. And he added ruefully, 'I daresay I shall be parting with a great deal more money for expenses incurred in this lunatic project of yours. Oh, and I've just remembered! What the devil do you mean by telling people it is *I* who am collecting donkeys?'

'I only told Elias,' laughed Kim. 'I thought he'd probably let me have it cheaper.'

'And did he?'

'I don't know.' Kim nestled in his arms and lifted her face. 'Vidas,' she said huskily, 'I love you.'

'My darling, I adore you!' Masterfully, he caught her to him, covering her eager lips with his, and within seconds she was being carried on the tide of his ardour until, needing breath himself, he slackened his hold.

Kim, still clinging to him, said provocatively, 'You haven't asked my why I changed my mind about giving you your freedom.'

'I'd never have taken my freedom, so it isn't important.' His warm hands were roving, caressing her lovely curves.

'It *is* important,' she insisted. 'You see, darling, something happened that made me think again—'

'Dearest Kim, I have said it isn't important,' Vidas bent his head to take her lips again, then tucked her arm in his and together they walked towards the door.

'All right,' said Kim with well-feigned indifference, 'it isn't important, so I won't bother telling you.'

He stopped abruptly by the door and glanced into her face. 'It obviously is important,' he began, then stopped as he noticed the delicate colour rising in her cheeks. 'Kim . . . my dearest wife . . . it's . . . ?'

'Yes,' she said with a lovely smile. 'So you see, darling, it *is* rather important, isn't it?'

Her husband made no answer but just looked at her adoringly for a long moment before lifting her hand to his lips.

IT'S YOUR OWN SPECIAL TIME

Contemporary romances for today's women.
Each month, six very special love stories will be yours
from SILHOUETTE. Look for them wherever books are sold
or order now from the coupon below.

$1.50 each

___#61 WHISPER MY NAME Michaels
___#62 STAND-IN BRIDE Halston
___#63 SNOWFLAKES IN THE SUN Brent
___#64 SHADOW OF APOLLO Hampson
___#65 A TOUCH OF MAGIC Hunter
___#66 PROMISES FROM THE PAST Vitek
___#67 ISLAND CONQUEST Hastings
___#68 THE MARRIAGE BARGAIN Scott
___#69 WEST OF THE MOON St. George
___#70 MADE FOR EACH OTHER Afton Bonds
___#71 A SECOND CHANCE ON LOVE Ripy
___#72 ANGRY LOVER Beckman
___#73 WREN OF PARADISE Browning
___#74 WINTER DREAMS Trent
___#75 DIVIDE THE WIND Carroll
___#76 BURNING MEMORIES Hardy
___#77 SECRET MARRIAGE Cork
___#78 DOUBLE OR NOTHING Oliver
___#79 TO START AGAIN Halldorson

___#80 WONDER AND WILD DESIRE Stephens
___#81 IRISH THOROUGHBRED Roberts
___#82 THE HOSTAGE BRIDE Dailey
___#83 LOVE LEGACY Halston
___#84 VEIL OF GOLD Vitek
___#85 OUTBACK SUMMER John
___#86 THE MOTH AND THE FLAME Adams
___#87 BEYOND TOMORROW Michaels
___#88 AND THEN CAME DAWN Stanford
___#89 A PASSIONATE BUSINESS James
___#90 WILD LADY Major
___#91 WRITTEN IN THE STARS Hunter
___#92 DESERT DEVIL McKay
___#93 EAST OF TODAY Browning
___#94 ENCHANTMENT Hampson
___#95 FOURTEEN KARAT BEAUTY Wisdom
___#96 LOVE'S TREACHEROUS JOURNEY Beckm
___#97 WANDERER'S DREAM Clay
___#98 MIDNIGHT WINE St. George
___#99 TO HAVE, TO HOLD Camp

$1.75 each

___#100 YESTERDAY'S SHADOW Stanford
___#101 PLAYING WITH FIRE Hardy
___#102 WINNER TAKE ALL Hastings
___#103 BY HONOUR BOUND Cork
___#104 WHERE THE HEART IS Vitek
___#105 MISTAKEN IDENTITY Eden
___#106 THE LANCASTER MEN Dailey
___#107 TEARS OF MORNING Bright
___#108 FASCINATION Hampson
___#109 FIRE UNDER SNOW Vernon
___#110 A STRANGER'S WIFE Trent
___#111 WAYWARD LOVER South

___#112 WHISPER WIND Stanford
___#113 WINTER BLOSSOM Browning
___#114 PAINT ME RAINBOWS Michaels
___#115 A MAN FOR ALWAYS John
___#116 AGAINST THE WIND Lindley
___#117 MANHATTAN MASQUERADE Scott
___#118 FOR THE LOVE OF GOD Dailey
___#119 DESIRE Hampson
___#120 TAKE THIS LOVE Carroll
___#121 JUST LIKE YESTERDAY Langan
___#122 WINTERFIRE Scofield
___#123 HOLIDAY IN JAMAICA Sinclair

Introducing
First Love from Silhouette Romances for teenage girls to build their dreams on.

They're wholesome, fulfilling, supportive novels about every young girl's dreams. Filled with the challenges, excitement— and responsibilities—of love's first blush, *First Love* paper-backs prepare young adults to stand at the threshold of maturity with confidence and composure.

Introduce your daughter, or some young friend to the *First Love* series by giving her a one-year subscription to these romantic originals, written by leading authors. She'll receive two NEW $1.75 romances each month, a total of 24 books a year. Send in your coupon now. **There's nothing quite as special as a First Love.**

Silhouette 🖤 *Romance*

15-Day Free Trial Offer
6 Silhouette Romances

6 Silhouette Romances, free for 15 days! We'll send you 6 new Silhouette Romances to keep for 15 days, absolutely free! If you decide not to keep them, send them back to us. You pay nothing.

Free Home Delivery. But if you enjoy them as much as we think you will, keep them by paying the invoice enclosed with your free trial shipment. We'll pay all shipping and handling charges. You get the convenience of Home Delivery and we pay the postage and handling charge each month.

Don't miss a copy. The Silhouette Book Club is the way to make sure you'll be able to receive every new romance we publish before they're sold out. There is no minimum number of books to buy and you can cancel at any time.

This offer expires May 31, 1982